LEONARDO'S MACHINES
Secrets and Inventions in the Da Vinci Codices

LEONARDO'S MACHINES
Secrets and Inventions in the Da Vinci Codices

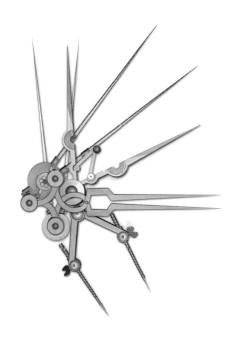

Edited by Mario Taddei and Edoardo Zanon

Text by
Domenico Laurenza

front cover
Three-dimensional reconstruction of Leonardo's automobile taken from folio 012r in the Codex Atlanticus.
back cover
Some of the parts of the machine.
frontispiece
Dividers reconstructed from folio 696r in the Codex Atlanticus.

Concept, mechanical philology and description of the machines
Mario Taddei *and* Edoardo Zanon

Editorial co-ordinator
Claudio Pescio

Editor
Ilaria Ferraris

Translation
Joan M. Reifsnyder

Technical layout supervision
Paola Zacchini

Introductory texts
Domenico Laurenza

Cover
Mario Taddei
Edoardo Zanon

Graphic design, layout and three-dimensional modelling
Giacomo Giannella, Felice Mancino
Gabriele Perni, Mario Taddei
Edoardo Zanon

Studioddm snc, via Malpighi 8, Milan
www.studioddm.com
www.leonardo3.net

For his collaboration, thanks go to
Giorgio Ferraris

Visit our website:
www.leonardonline.en

www.giunti.it

© 2005 Giunti Editore S.p.A.
Via Bolognese 165 - 50139 Florence - Italy
Via Dante 4 - 20121 Milan - Italy
© 2005 Studioddm S.n.c., Milan

3	
Reprints	Year
10 9 8 7 6 5	2014 2013 2012 2011

Printed at Giunti Industrie Grafiche S.p.A., Prato

The translation of this work has been funded by SEPS
SEGRETARIATO EUROPEO PER LE PUBBLICAZIONI SCIENTIFICHE

Via Val d'Aposa 7 - 40123 Bologna - Italy
seps@alma.unibo.it - www.seps.it

Leonardo's manuscripts and drawings, all available in the Edizione Nazionale Vinciana (Giunti), are cited according to usual practice as follows:

Codex Atlanticus	Codex Atlanticus in the Biblioteca Ambrosiana, Milan
Windsor RL	Anatomical manuscripts and drawings in the Royal Library at Windsor Castle
Codex Arundel	Codex Ardunel 263 in the British Library, London (formerly the British Museum Library)
Codex Forster I–III	Notebooks in the library at the Victoria and Albert Museum, London
Manuscripts Madrid I & II	Codices in the Biblioteca Nacional, Madrid
Manuscripts A–M	Codices and notebooks in the library of the Institute de France, Paris
Codex Hammer	Manuscript (formerly Codex Leicester) owned by Bill Gates, Seattle, Washington, USA
Codex Trivulzianus	Manuscript in the Biblioteca Trivulziana at the Castello Sforzesco, Milan
Codex 'On the Flight of Birds'	Manuscript at the Biblioteca Reale, Turin

The chronology of Leonardo's notes and drawings varies even within a single manuscript; thus, the exact or approximate date is given for each reproduced image.

Contents

Presentation

Over the past century, Leonardo's extraordinary machines have been the object of growing attention that has often become almost obsessive in dimension. In recent years the production of books, catalogues and pamphlets promising to reveal the sensational advances made by the Genius from Vinci has intensified. At the same time there has been a proliferation of haphazard and out-of-context exhibitions on 'Leonardo the confused inventor' (not to mention the pseudo 'museums' on Leonardo, carelessly installed with ever-increasing frequency in historical cities), produced by improvised curators who with impunity challenge the lairs of the complex Da Vincian world.

In the context of this intense but generally poor-quality offer signalling the vigorous reprisal of 'Leonardo-mania' and whetted by the success of the Dan Brown's whimsical journey into an imaginary Da Vincian world, the contributions made in this volume by Domenico Laurenza, Mario Taddei and Edoardo Zanon are clearly different for a number of significant reasons.

The first of these is the translation of the results of Leonardo's technical drawings into the extraordinarily effective visual language of computer graphics. If in these translation operations there is the inevitable transfiguration of the original document, it is legitimatised in the effort to render intelligible the meaning of the complex technological analyses developed by Leonardo. Thus, if we are speaking, and rightly so, about transfiguration, then it should be mentioned that the ' slippage' of the original drawing to a reconfiguration using a superior means of graphic perspective must be considered as the metamorphosis and development of the same intent and communicative methodologies pursued by Leonardo.

The extraordinary mechanical graphics perfected by Taddei and Zanon lead to a more penetrating and universally understood level of effective explanation. Now, the very same experiments in graphic communication, conceived by Leonardo in his manuscripts in order to visualise analytical processes and the results of his own thought process and innovative concepts in relation to machines and mechanical devices, can be understood and appreciated. In fact, the mechanical iconographic album that gives this volume its unique character fully realises Leonardo's goal of supplying a complete and absolutely clear representation of the structure and the workings of extremely complex devices. He resorts to a series of graphic conventions (plane and overhead views, views in transparency, exploded views, simulations in kinematic sequence, the use of *chiaroscuro* in highlighting contact surfaces, schematic representation of force lines, etc.) that no one before him had conceived of as an organised unit, and above all, had knowingly applied to a communications project in the complex sphere of technology.

The beautiful Da Vincian machines, translated into a digital language laid out on the centre of the pages in this evocative book, therefore reflect Leonardo's own ideal concept of nature and his goals in graphically representing machines. These 'dissected' machines, examined in transparency and knowingly 'exploded' to reveal the hidden mechanisms, vie with Leonardo's original, masterly drawings both in fascination and beauty. Even though they may lack the magical, evocative character of the documents written in the Maestro's inimitable hand, they nonetheless surpass them in explicative effectiveness and didacticism.

Along with the bold, but essentially respectful, operation of translating Leonardo's original drawings into three-dimensional visualisations using computer graphics, the choice of the mechanical devices illustrated in this volume was neither stereotyped nor repetitive.

The vast production of traditional catalogues and pamphlets dedicated to Leonardo's machines has as its common trait the obsessive replication of a fairly circumscript number of Leonardo's machines. Machines that constitute a well-consolidated unit upon which his reputation rests as Leonardo the sensationally precocious inventor of the most important discoveries in the modern era: the flying machine, the submarine, the helicopter, the armoured tank, the automobile, and more recently even the much-discussed 'bicycle'.

In our volume the horizon broadens. As a result of very careful examination of the Da Vincian manuscripts by Taddei and Zanon, correlated by the essential critical and philological contributions by Laurenza, the reader is presented with a choice that differs significantly from the repetitive catalogues currently available. Thus the reader discovers new devices, not always precursory and sensational inventions, but nonetheless emblematic evidence of unexpected technical problems that Leonardo tried to solve, employing ingenious solutions albeit extremely problematic to put into practice.

Even in those cases when the most universally celebrated inventions are presented, in our volume these are critically illustrated, put in context, and above all, technically analysed in a way that is not at all commonplace. The drawings for some of the studies on the flying machine as well as the project where Leonardo's so-called 'automobile' is presented offer eloquent examples of this approach, based on the combination of historical rigour and the effort to perfect an effective strategy of visual communication.

In the first case, it is important to point out the useful and programmed interaction between the introduction and the philological briefs by Domenico Laurenza, (where the original documents are placed in context, given a chronology clearly illustrating their purposes, and tied to analogous studies in other Vinciana manuscripts), and the evocative visualisations by Taddei and Zanon. These visuals appear as a morphing of Leonardo's often-cryptic sketches into transparent representations that delineate the operating mechanisms and that clearly simulate the complex functions using cinematic-like sequences taking on the tangible form of real models, thanks to the three-dimensional visualisations in perspective.

In terms of the so-called 'automobile', it should be pointed out how the incredible work of translating Leonardo's complex drawing into an understandable representation of the innovative device, exact in every minute detail, simulates with extraordinary perspicacity the complex process of transmitting energy produced by spring-driven motors. This is a result of lengthy research initiated by Carlo Pedretti's illuminated intuition and transformed by Mark Rosheim into the first plausible interpretation of the vehicle based on engineering principles. The work put in by Taddei and Zanon has definitively clarified not only the structure and the workings of the programmable cart conceived by Leonardo around 1478, but also confirms that the bold device should almost certainly be recognised as an instrument destined to produce amazing effects at Renaissance court festivals.

Thanks to the co-operation between Taddei and Zanon and the Istituto e Museo di Storia della Scienza in Florence (along with the determinative support of the Banca di Credito Cooperativo di Cambiano), it was possible to make perfectly functioning real and virtual models of Leonardo's automobile, on display in a scientifically rigorous and enormously successful world-travelling exhibition (see: http://brunelleschi.imss.fi.it/automobile). As can be seen on the pages in this volume dedicated to the 'automobile', Taddei and Zanon have elaborated and realised an extraordinarily evocative graphic code of communication. Thanks to this code, even a reader who is not an expert in mechanical structures can grasp the complex processes and the refined technological solutions behind the workings of the Da Vincian device.

The integration of Domenico Laurenza's precise introductions and descriptive entries with the digitally-elaborated matrix of visuals by Taddei and Zanon formulate convincing and didactically effective results for all Leonardo's machines illustrated in this volume. The iconographical images are not meant to propose only three-dimensional representations; they also provide a careful and minute dissection of the devices, isolating the parts and components, each one distinctly represented. The reader is provided with an evocative graphic kit that facilitates an imaginary assembling and disassembling of the devices.

In addition to the aesthetic fascination and the extraordinary didactic and demonstrative effectiveness of this method, it must be stressed that our approach corresponds to Leonardo's same aspirations. He conceived the drawing of a machine as an instrument for analysing the most complex devices down to the last part, accurately 'dissecting' them in order to obtain a representation that was both analytical and synthetic. With the same lucidity, Leonardo made the unheard of effort of using drawing to give the machines not simply an inexpressive statue-like appearance, but also to effectively suggest the dynamics of their workings, simulating with static images the transmission of their movements using their various mechanical components.

It is worth pointing out that above all, the Da Vincian representations of machines make a revolutionary contribution because they are configured as 'almost dynamic' images, extraordinary precursors of the drawing methods used in animation, and especially the kinematic modelling used in computer graphics. The transposition of Leonardo's original drawings in the context of new media representations completes Leonardo's own aspirations. His were the first drawings to express the need for a new concept in technological imaging, understood as the design of an integrated circuit of knowledge, able to show how the machine appears externally, the mechanical principles that govern its workings and the analytical construction of its organs.

In this new concept of design, one of Leonardo's most pathbreaking precedents must be identified, more concrete and plausible than all the amazing inventions boldly attributed to him: he was the first to conceive of machine design as a refined tool for analysis and research, to be used even before its visualisation for purely demonstrative ends. This volume edited by Giunti helps us to understand that one of the essential passages in Leonardo's fundamental contribution to the modern culture of machines is the mature elaboration of a specific technical language: an exquisitely visual language that he forced himself to articulate using strict grammar and syntax.

Paolo Galluzzi
Director of the Istituto e Museo di Storia della Scienza, Florence

Introduction

Today, only the drawings of Leonardo's machines remain. Even if one of his mechanical projects had been translated into an actual object, none of them have survived. Nor do we have any of his three-dimensional models, which he surely must have constructed in the design phase between the drawing and the real machine. The same is true for some of his paintings like the *Battle of Anghiari*: we have numerous drawings but not the final work.

Nevertheless, if time had preserved one of his machines instead of its relative drawing, our loss would have been far greater. Mechanical design for Leonardo belongs to a very cerebral dimension, which through drawing finds it most ideal and complete (almost) form of expression. The understanding of the intrinsic content in a mechanical drawing, the purpose of the machine and the way it was meant to work, the relationship between its parts, may have been enough for many inventors in the past. In Leonardo's case it is only one of the two aspects of the game, and not the main one. For him what really mattered was to grasp the entire meaning behind the drawn forms: the theories that generated a mechanical design and the graphic means giving shape to those theories. Many of the machines designed by Leonardo – the most spectacular ones – are nothing more than the visual or material forms of his scientific experiments; theories expressed not by words but by images. For example, the so-called flying ship drawn on one of the sheets in Manuscript B (f. 80r, in the same group of drawings as the flying machines), is the culmination of a series of studies Leonardo had dedicated to the dynamic potentialities of the human body, that is, its capacity to generate force. Before being the design for a flying machine, this drawing is the design of a device to allow a man closed in the centre of a cockpit to generate force using every part of his body. From this point of view the oneiric character of some machines, the technological dream of actually working many Da Vincian devices, finds partial explanation. In fact, the elective space of Leonardo's machines is not so much real space as it is drawn space, the image and its virtual dimension.

The intellectual value in drawing was widely affirmed during the *Quattrocento*. Roberto Valturio (1405-1475) in his *De re militari* reconstructed the war machines of the ancients resorting extensively to the use of images, so much so that they became a humanistic philological tool. Francesco di Giorgio (1439-1501) clearly identified in mechanical drawing a tool for intellectual expression and a means of affirming the professional emancipation of technicians and engineers, who until that time were considered artisans. But he also affirmed the irreplaceable role of the three-dimensional model during the design phases of a machine. He writes: 'it is difficult to show every thing in a drawing because so many varieties of pieces are interrupted and on top of one another that to draw them all is impossible, and so, it is necessary to make a model for practically each thing' (*Treatise on Architecture*).

This limitation is certainly overcome by Leonardo, who even though he uses three-dimensional models in various aspects of his research (machines, painting, anatomy), he seems to give drawing the primary position over models, recognising both its design and cognitive values.

A famous section in the *Lives* by Giorgio Vasari describes the nature of drawing, and cites a Greek proverb: a skilful drawer, observing only the depiction of a single part of the whole, is perfectly able to reconstruct the whole in form and dimension; the vision of a fragment of sculpture representing only the claw of a lion is sufficient to perfectly reconstruct the entire lion. According to Vasari, this is manifestation and proof of the mental strength of those who practice drawing. Vasari wants to demonstrate that even though achieved manually, drawing is primarily an intellectual activity. Vasari writes: 'From this cognisance a certain concept and judgement of the thing is created in the mind, and that which is then expressed through the hands is called drawing'. In the mid-sixteenth century Vasari definitively sanctions a lofty concept of graphic arts and its activity; an activity that was Leonardo's greatest form of expression if only because of the many areas where he applied it: not only art, but science and technical fields as well.

In order to comprehend the intellectual value in Leonardo's drawing, the contraposition between drawing and Leonardo's concept of painting is very significant. It is well known that Leonardo is the inventor of the *sfumato* painting technique, and he abhors that the painted figure should be closed within lines and sharp limits. In fact, based on optical considerations (in reality the eye never sees sharp lines) as well as more philosophical considerations, he believes that it is impossible to define the surface or the outline of a body as real. He writes: 'The external limits of a thing are not at all part of the thing itself, because the end of one thing is the beginning of another [...] and thus these ends occupy nothing'. Where the body ends is where the air surrounding it begins: thus the external limits of a body, from a theoretical viewpoint, do not exist in and of itself. If the external limits of things themselves do not exist, this means that when he draws Leonardo is well aware that he is doing more than 'photographically' portraying what is real: he studies reality or he reinvents it, he makes an abstraction. A painted figure in imitating reality can not have any trace of the drawing; a machine, in its drawn state, belongs to a mental, abstract dimension, and judging from the 'realism' of his designs, this merits consideration.

While he is in Rome (circa 1513-1516) as guest of the Florentine pope Leo X, Leonardo's life is afflicted by a difficult relationship with a technician called-in by Giuliano de' Medici, brother to the pontiff and Leonardo's patron. 'Giorgio Tedesco' (George the German) – this is the name of the assistant – insists on a higher salary than what was agreed upon. Instead of working in the workshop, he goes about wasting time, and worst of all he reveals to others the secrets and inventions of the *maestro*. As a result of this, in a shrewd letter addressed to Giuliano de' Medici, Leonardo inserts a very interesting note: 'Then the request of this person was to have *models made of wood* as he wanted them in iron, which he wanted to take to his country. I denied this to him saying that I would give the *drawing* of the width, length and size and figure of that which he had to do; and thus we did not remain on good terms' (Codex Atlanticus, f. 671r, author's italics). This affirmation is very important, and if correctly deciphered, it can furnish some interesting information. Tedesco asks Leonardo to provide him with three-dimensional wooden models of a few of the mechanical devices that would then be made in iron. Leonardo refuses to give him the models, offering instead drawings indicating the 'width, length, size and shape' of the machines; drawings that were probably in perspective and/or multiple views, from which the information on how to make the machine could be obtained. Still, in view of the circumstances and given Leonardo's mistrust for Tedesco, the fact that Leonardo intended to supply drawings instead of three-dimensional models may indicate something else. Giorgio Tedesco had asked for three-dimensional wooden models because he was able to copy these in order to reconstruct the machines using metal. It must have been more difficult for him to interpret scale drawings. In order to understand them he needed the help of the *maestro*; he needed Leonardo's help. By giving Tedesco the drawings instead of the models, Leonardo could let him work without revealing too much about the project. We are faced with another indication of the value Leonardo placed on drawing: it is something more than a simple three-dimensional model, to be understood it requires a special theoretical background (for example, the proportional relationships between the parts). The use of drawings instead of wooden models made the difference between an evolved engineering studio, where the engineer considered himself to be a man with a mind in addition to his hands, and a traditional-type workshop.

The machines that Leonardo designed can be studied and presented as three-dimensional reconstructions, even as interactive models, as found in some museums and exhibitions. These reconstructions have to do with the intrinsic content of the machine, its practical side. Studies have generally given preference to understanding only the practical side of Leonardo's inventions. Up to now less attention has been dedicated to the intellectual aspect of Leonardo's drawings, which, as stated before, is its most important aspect. Is it possible to present and reconstruct Leonardo's mechanical projects highlighting the graphic side as well? In this book Mario Taddei and Edoardo Zanon have made reconstructions of Leonardo's machines that although they are virtually three-dimensional models (thus attentive to the mechanical significance of the project), they use a wide spectra of visual solutions (multiple view points, exploded views, directional arrows, etc.) that emphasise the drawing aspect in Leonardo's elaborations. The written introduction to each individual project (elaborated by this writer) about the formal aspects of the drawings, takes this same direction.

With regard to the presentation in museums of Da Vincian inventions (that can be extended to all other types of intervention. exhibitions, books, etc.), Paolo Galluzzi has recently spoken about a desirable 'Copernican revolution' that consists in placing Leonardo's drawings as the central axis, with the models taking on a subordinate role. Without losing sight of the mechanical significance of each project, the intent of this book is to experiment the possibility of just such a revolution.

Domenico Laurenza

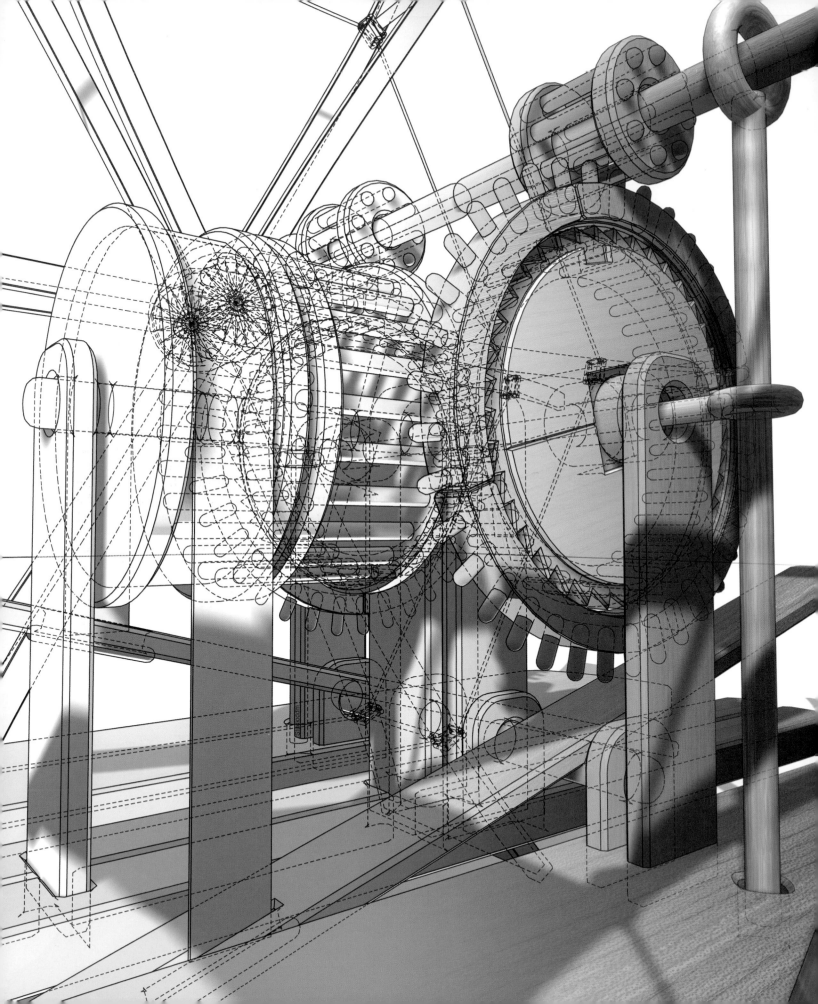

Introduction

left
*Technical detail
of the paddleboat
using pedal propulsion
(see p. 141).*

A new book on Leonardo's machines? Did the most well-known scientific figure of all times really need a new volume illustrating his projects? Just another of the same kind of book with the same machines everyone knows?

Leonardo's scientific and technical patrimony is an endless resource and treasure-trove of ideas and intuitions, and it is difficult to imagine that the full *oeuvre* of this scientist can ever be completely grasped. Even the most well-known machines, even the most carefully reconstructed physical models on display in the important exhibitions still hide secrets that can always be extracted. Even today these Renaissance projects continue to amaze those who study and analyse them. Anyone who, like ourselves, begins to discover Leonardo is especially drawn-in by the realisation that they will never reach the true end of a project. As often happened while preparing this book, even when it seemed as if the correct interpretation of a mechanism or an entire project had been reached, another squiggle on the page or analogous drawing from another manuscript opened new solutions making further clarification and surprising evolutions possible. It is also possible that a totally convincing structural idea or particular function of a machine can be put in doubt by a single detail, discovered at the last moment, a detail that redirects the entire interpretation of a mechanism or the entire machine in a completely different direction. This same type of discovery occurred during the studies on Leonardo's so-called 'automobile', presented in our joint project with the Istituto e Museo di Storia della Scienza in Florence and published in this volume. The interpretation of the machine was unravelled after almost a century of attempts made by numerous Da Vincian scholars such as Semenza and Canestrini, to mention only a couple. When we began our work, together with the museum, on interpreting the machine we were inevitably fascinated and struck by the fact that by correctly following all Leonardo's sketches and lines, everything fit precisely into place in the drawn project; a realisation that probably did not occur in previously developed solutions. One has to keep in mind that models made prior to 2004 and presented in many museums do not reflect Leonardo's true idea, and essentially, they do not work. We began from a very solid base: the correct interpretation made by Mark Rosheim on one hand, and the invaluable advise from Paolo Galluzzi and Carlo Pedretti on the other, making it possible to accurately prepare our first study models for the prototype and the construction of the final models; perhaps not aesthetically outstanding, but completely functional from their very first assembly. When the work was almost completed, and the functioning, exhibition automobile was already in the produc-

fig. 1
*Folio 812r
in the Codex Atlanticus.*

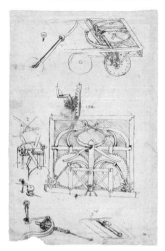

tion phase at the Laboratori Fiorentini, almost by chance while observing a drawing in the margin of the manuscript we discovered that it represented a brake. (What a memorable moment!) A very quick sketch on the lower part of the page concealed this small device. As testimony to the importance of even a small set of lines by Leonardo, this detail added a new element to the project, and even more important, it further verified its interpretation. Not an 'automobile' by today's concept, meant to transport persons or things, but a theatrical device. It was probably a more ambitious and certainly a more complex project: a machine that could be programmed and was meant to be used for special scene effects. The very same detail also revealed how the operator worked the machine. Hidden in the wings and by pulling a cord, the operator released the small brake so that the machine moved towards the audience on its own.

In putting together this book more than fifty interpretations were necessary, all made with the same critical spirit as the episode mentioned above and always waiting for the surprising detail confirming or revealing possible new solutions for the project. Often we realised that some machines, even the most 'famous', had not been completely understood. The mechanisms and projects in this book represent only a detailed synthesis of the material under examination. It required more than a year to identify the subjects, understand them, reconstruct them and depict them. Computer graphics, and more generally, computer technology are certainly not new to the technical world, however, we believe that this same language can be used in a very original way for rendering the *maestro's* ideas visible. The tools used to compose the images are very similar, and in some cases the same, to those used to create commercial video games or for special effects in movies and new types of animated cartoons. The novelty of this volume is that these techniques have been adopted to construct a new visual language. Not a paradigmatic revolution but a go-between, linking the institutional world of culture – the world of the Vinciana readings, the historical books on Leonardo, the most recent exhibitions – and today's world of young people, the same individuals who spend hours playing on the computer or with the *PlayStation*. One wonders what Leonardo might have been able to do with modern multimedia and design tools. Perhaps the distance between Leonardo and the world of video games is closer than it may seem: looking at some of his projects, for example the crane for canals, the file-cutting machine, the swing bridge and many others, one inevitably becomes enchanted by the immediacy of the drawing, Leonardo's simple and direct way of communicating, knowingly given to each page. 'O poet, what letters will you use to

figs. 2 and 3
Folio CA 1r drawn by Leonardo and the 3D model of the barrage cannon superimposed on the original drawing.

write that have the same perfection as drawing in describing the whole figure?', the *maestro* writes on Windsor 19071r, RL.

As soon as a model is finished, we superimpose it on the original drawing, and often we observe a surprising congruence in the parts. This operation takes on great importance for those of us who draw without the use of a pencil, using intangible instruments. It is precisely in this moment that we understand we are on the right path, that we are using the correct instruments to disclose the workings of the machine, a path Leonardo would certainly have shared. With computer and digital technology we move towards his way of designing; the third dimension was certainly in Leonardo's mind while he drew, and hence the name of our site dedicated to him, www.leonardo3.net.

This book visually 'narrates' more than thirty machines by Leonardo Da Vinci, some of them never before published. In reality, there are many more manuscripts involved in this study and in the production of this volume than the number of actual machines on these pages. This is due to the fact that the correct understanding of the workings of a machine requires an in-depth documentation and a broad vision of all the works by Leonardo.

A special word of thanks must go to Sergio Giunti, Paolo Galluzzi, Carlo Pedretti and Claudio Pescio who believed in this book, and to the individuals who worked with us and contributed to the project: Felice Mancino, Gabriele Perni, Giacomo Giannella, Cristina Caramori and Michela Baldessari.

Mario Taddei
Edoardo Zanon

Figurative Index

001 **Flying Machines**

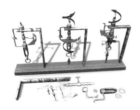   

Mechanisms for Mechanical Wings	**Dragonfly**	**Flapping Wing**	**Aerial Screw**
Codex Atlanticus, f. 1051v 1480-1485	Ashburnham I, f. 10v circa 1487	Manuscript B, f. 88v 1487-1489	Manuscript B, f. 83v circa 1489

Mechanisms for transforming reciprocating or circular motion in the mechanical movements of the various wing parts. Many of these are described on this folio in the Codex Atlanticus: these and other drawings are the basis for understanding the complex functioning of Leonardo's projects for flight.

This was originally the first folio in Manuscript B, the work Leonardo dedicated primarily to the study of possible flying machines. It is presumed that the genius from Vinci began studies for these machines inspired by nature, observing insects and flying creatures, in this case the dragonfly.

An experimental machine used to verify the capacity of human force to flap with enough energy to move the wing. Another interpretation is that the machine could have been useful in verifying the behaviour of the wing itself during the powerful movements required for its use.

Usually held to be the forerunner of the modern helicopter, this project is interesting not as much for the mechanical solutions as for the simile made to water; Leonardo perceived air as a thinner dynamic fluid through which the machine could 'screw' or twist itself: for this reason a more correct term is 'aerial screw' rather than 'helicopter'.

- | page 30 | -   - | page 34 | -   - | page 38 | -   - | page 46 | -

Flying Machine	**Mechanical Wings**	**Springald**	**Multi-barrelled Machine Gun**
Manuscript B, f. 74v 1488-1489	Codex Atlanticus, f. 844r 1493-1495	Codex Atlanticus, f. 32r circa 1482	Codex Atlanticus, f. 157r circa 1482

A complete study for the flying machine: after studying many devices, Leonardo begins more than one project for a flying machine. This drawing clearly shows the position of the pilot-driver as well as the operations that must be carried out in order to manoeuvre and (presumably) keep the device in flight.

A small-scale model for studying the flapping of wings. The machine itself is quite complex due to the fact that various mechanisms are used to convert the rotating motion of a hand crank into the reciprocating linear motion of the flapping wing. This mechanical wing faithfully simulates the articulations and movement dynamics of the wing in nature, where the extremities of the wings make curving movements different from those at the base of the wing.

Among the many plans for military projects an entire portion was dedicated to the concept and development of cannons. These springalds allowed the gunner to position the cannon before firing without having to move the entire structure: in fact, the cannon could be swung around and inclined as desired in order to aim in different directions. A protective, wooden housing was also designed to cover the weapon.

This machine gun had considerable firepower. Once the cannons were loaded and ready to be fired a broad range of fire was ensured. Because the gun carriage was easily moveable, it could be aimed at different objectives as necessary. The altitude of the cannon fire could be adjusted using a hand crank on the rear of the carriage.

- | page 54 | -   - | page 62 | -   - | page 74 | -   - | page 80 | -

Defence of the Walls	Scythed Chariots	Dismountable Cannon	Armoured Car

Codex Atlanticus, f. 139r
1482-1485

Turin, Bibl. Reale,
f. 15583r
circa 1485

Codex Atlanticus, f. 154br
1478-1485

London, British Museum,
Popham no. 1030
circa 1485

Leonardo designed not only attack artillery, but also complex and ingenious methods of defence. Here, when the walls are under attack, the soldiers hidden behind the battlements could quickly and easily ward-off enemies and their attack structures in a single movement by using a system of levers.

Perhaps made to impress Ludovico il Moro, this is one of Leonardo's most beautiful manuscripts. These plans show scythed chariots for use in battle. Drawn by running horses, these machines with their sharp, cutting blades moved in the thick of the battle slashing through all in their wake.

Cannons were very heavy and the carriages used to transport them were often unwieldy. Leonardo designed a structure that could be easily dismantled and transported, thus permitting the cannon to be easily moved.

This is one of Leonardo's most well-known projects. The idea of an armoured car protected by a giant shield, having notable firepower and easily positioned on the battlefield was an ambitious project even for the genius from Vinci. Even with modifications the plan still had a number of unresolved problems. Faced with practically insurmountable difficulties, Leonardo abandoned the project.

-| page 84 |-   -| page 88 |-   -| page 94 |-   -| page 98 |-

| Catapult | Barrage Cannon | Bombards in action | Fortress |

Codex Atlanticus,
f. 140ar e 140br
1485-1490

Codex Atlanticus, f. 1ar
1503-1505

Codex Atlanticus, f. 33r
circa 1504

Codex Atlanticus, f. 117r
1507-1510

There are many plans for catapults. This particular design uses a double leaf spring to produce an enormous amount of energy for propelling stone projectiles or incendiary materials, over great distances. The loading of the two large leaf springs was accomplished using a hand crank on the side of the catapult.

This drawing is on the first page of the Codex Atlanticus. The drawing itself is very complete and quite fascinating; it illustrates the plan of a bombard with sixteen radial cannons. The most interesting aspect of the project is the centre of the bombard itself, housing a pair of mechanical paddles and gear wheels, providing only a partial idea of the possibilities of this huge structure. There can certainly be more than one interpretation.

This is a drawing of rare beauty and extreme clarity. The folio shows two bombards at the moment they are being fired. In addition to the plan for the bombard, a weapon already known at the time, Leonardo also designed the large projectiles, which once they were fired exploded into many fragments with greater range and impact than the cannonball itself.

Leonardo designed this project of a very compact fortress with the idea of rendering it safe from attack: the elaborate shape is innovative and presumably can effectively defend against the impact of the new, deadly artillery projectiles.

- | page 102 | -   - | page 108 | -   - | page 118 | -   - | page 126 | -

003 **Hydraulic Machines**

Mechanical Saw	**Paddleboat**	**Swing Bridge**	**Dredger**
Codex Atlanticus, f. 1078ar circa 1478	Codex Atlanticus, f. 945r 1487-1489	Codex Atlanticus, f. 855r 1487-1489	Manuscript E, f. 75v 1513-1514

This machine is used for cutting large tree-trunks; the movement of water, presumably channelled through a mill, worked the large paddle wheel that furnished the energy required to move the blade. At the same time the water-propelled wheel moved a series of pulleys that pulled the heavy trunk positioned on a moveable bed through the saw.

Leonardo designed a boat that could easily navigate using a system more practical than oars. In fact, oars need to be moved using a repetitive action producing discontinuous energy. With paddles however, the operators use their feet (or, in other models, their arms) to move the large side wheels, making the craft move without interruption.

This bridge is beautifully designed. A support structure constructed around a large pivot pin positioned on one of the riverbanks permitted the passage of both land and water transport. The bridge rotated around the main pivot pin, and was set into motion by one or more persons operating the winches positioned on land.

The dredger was used to widen and clean riverbeds. The idea for this machine already existed prior to this project, but Leonardo introduced important technical enhancements. For example, he gave the craft more stability by equipping it with two hulls instead of just one.

- | page 134 | -   - | page 140 | -   - | page 146 | -   - | page 156 | -

Reciprocating Motion Machine

Codex Atlanticus, f. 30v
1478-1480

This project studies the transformation of reciprocating motion into continuous motion. In this machine power is produced to lift a heavy body from the ground. By moving a lever back and forth, the operator activates the mechanism that allows the line to wind around the centre-rotating shaft.

File-cutter

Codex Atlanticus, f. 24r
circa 1480

This machine automatically cut files. Due to its weight and thus the force of gravity, a weight suspended from a line made it move. By activating various mechanisms, the file advanced and at the same time was struck by an attached hammer. With every blow by the iron hammer, a cut was made in the metal file.

Device for Grinding Concave Mirrors

Codex Atlanticus, f. 87r
circa 1480

By activating a single hand crank, the rotating motion was transferred simultaneously onto two stone disks positioned on two different axes. The respective rotatory motion of the disks hollowed and smoothed out the mirror placed on the horizontal disk.

Canal Excavating Crane

Codex Atlanticus, f. 4r
1503-1504

With this project, Leonardo meant to excavate riverbeds in order to change the course of the water using a crane having greater efficiency than contemporary machines. In fact, this device could slowly advance forward as the excavation proceeded and rendered the transportation of the material from the canal very fast and practical.

- | page 164 | -   - | page 168 | -   - | page 172 | -   - | page 176 | -

005 Theatrical Machines

006 Musical Instruments

Self-propelled Cart

Theatrical Staging for Orpheus

Skull-shaped Lyre

Mechanical Drum

Codex Atlanticus, f. 812r
1478-1480

Codex Arundel, f. 231v
circa 1507

Ashburnham I, f. Cr
1485-1487

Codex Atlanticus, f. 837r
1503-1505

This was not an automobile destined to transport persons or things; it was even more ambitious. It was a theatrical device that could be programmed, capable of moving on its own, not only in a straight-line but also following a curved path. This object is certainly one of Leonardo's most fascinating devices, appearing on stage alone before the audience's eyes, without a driver and without anyone pushing it.

Leonardo designed many theatrical devices. In this project ingenious stage sets appeared during the theatrical scenes. This particular set was used in staging *Orpheus*.

A design for a lyre that was most probably meant for use on stage rather than an instrument to be actually played. The idea of using animal parts as sound boxes in musical instruments has prehistoric origins.

The mechanical drum was most likely conceived for use in parades and processions along the city streets. But it may have been used in military parades or even in war, inciting the soldiers to battle or in intimidating the enemy. In fact, Leonardo's design has some variations on the basic project: a person or animal could draw the cart and a simple crank could also work it.

- | page 188 | -   - | page 196 | -   - | page 206 | -   - | page 210 | -

Viola Organista	Printing Press	Odometer	Compasses & Dividers
Codex Atlanticus, f. 93r 1493-1495	Codex Atlanticus, f. 995r 1478-1482	Codex Atlanticus, f. 1br circa 1504	Codex Atlanticus, f. 696b 1514-1515

This is a very complex project for an instrument that is difficult to categorise. It could be worn using a simple harness and is played with a keyboard. An internal, continually moving bow made from horsehair touches the cords moved by the keyboard. The sliding action of the looping bow on the strings emitted a sound more like a violin than a harpsichord.

An automatic bed connected to a pressure system permitted the printer to print and advance the sheet of paper in a single operation by moving a large lever on the front.

This strange vehicle was drawn by a person over a specific area in order to measure distances. A complex mechanism let a metal or wooden sphere drop into a container every time a given distance was travelled. Once the course was completed, the operator only had to count the number of spheres in the container in order to calculate the distance covered.

This is a small collection of work instruments, among them some dividers and compasses. One of the most fascinating aspects of Leonardo's work is the marriage between function and aesthetics in many of the devices he invented. These objects are perfect examples.

- | page 216 | -   - | page 226 | -   - | page 230 | -   - | page 234 | -

001 **Flying Machines**

Perhaps the oldest group of studies related to a flying machine is found on a folio in the Uffizi (447E). Most likely these studies by Leonardo, as well as similar ones from the same period, are all part of his designs for *'ingegni'*, that is, theatrical machines designed in Florentine workshops. In Florence, engineers and artists such as Brunelleschi and Verrocchio had great success with these types of projects. Leonardo is strongly dependent on this context, but equally strong is his intention to surpass it. On this same folio from the Uffizi we find a trace of his intent, a small but very clear trace. On the verso of the folio, Leonardo has drawn the diving trajectory of a bird in flight with annotated comments. His study thus moves away from the empirical and mechanical dimension to a different level, one more theoretical and zoological. When Leonardo decides to go to Milan, offering his services as engineer to Ludovico il Moro, he makes no mention of flying machines in his letter of presentation. We can perhaps glean from this that at least in his mind the project was still part of the realm of theatrical sets. Or even more simply, perhaps a flying machine would have seemed useless or something totally mad. What is certain however, is that human flight was already on the minds of the most advanced machinators centuries before. There are records of more or less empirical attempts at flight, which from a scientific viewpoint had little significance. It should be remembered, however, that in the thirteenth century the great natural philosopher, Roger Bacon, mentions the possibility of man flying with the use of mechanical wings. Further, in the fourteenth century, the sculpted panels depicting various industrial activities on the base of Giotto's Bell Tower include the myth of Daedalus: a human figure with wings tied to his shoulders. Certainly, it was only a mythical figure. Nonetheless the idea of human flight, even though utopian in character, existed in the vibrant environment in which Florentine engineers were immersed; it was Leonardo who would take it seriously and develop it into scientific form. This development takes place after his transfer to Milan. Differently from what we might expect, the main scientific field connected to Leonardo's projects on flying machines during the 1480s and 1490s is not zoology. During this period, his studies on the animal world are temporarily set aside, to be taken up again after 1500. At the close of the fifteenth century, Leonardo begins the design for his flying machine with man. His projects are rooted in the convergence of two fields of study: anatomy and mechanics (the study of weights and movement). On one hand, Leonardo studies the anatomical structure of the human body and its proportions. On the other, he studies the behaviour of weights, the dynamic and kinematic characteristics of movement. In this latter environment, the science of *'de ponderibus'* already had an illustrious tradition, which however remained an abstract discipline, rarely applied to real life objects. Already in the 1480s, Leonardo studies and measures the dynamic potentialities of the human body. He compiles pages and pages of drawings where the human body is shown in various postures and spatial situations, all with the purpose of sampling the body's capacity to generate force. Many of the projects from this period for the flying machine are the applications of these studies relating to the dynamic potential of the human body. For example, the famous project for the 'ornithopter' has very little to do with the animal world (Manuscript B, f. 80r). The alternating flapping of the wings was certainly similar to some insects, nevertheless, just by the shape of this machine (a motorised mechanism with a pilot and wings placed in a hemispherical-shaped hull) it was clear that it had very little to do with zoology. The key is in understanding how it operates. Leonardo uses a complex mechanical system for maximising the dynamic potentialities of the pilot's body, which has to generate force not only with the arms but also using legs and head. There is no trace of a steering mechanism. He becomes almost an 'automatic' pilot, whose only function is to generate sufficient force to flap the wings and lift off the ground. Turning manoeuvres are problems dealt with in another group of projects, projects in which the pilot is in a horizontal position (for example, Codex Atlanticus f. 824v and Manuscript B f. 79r). In this group of studies there is also greater attention to natural flight, however, it is important to note that despite some drawings (for example, Codex Atlanticus ff. 70br and 846v), rarely does Leonardo propose a synthesis between projects centred around the generation of force for flying and projects dealing with turning manoeuvres. In Florence during the early 1500s, Leonardo resumes the study of human flight in a systematic fashion. Nature, zoology, the study of the natural flight of birds now takes on an importance it did not previously have. Leonardo spends hour after hour outdoors observing the flight techniques of birds. Some of his codices dating from this time period are in fact pocket notebooks, in which Leonardo quickly and directly jots down notes and sketches on what he is observing. Manuscript L and Manuscript K1 are small codices of this type. It is therefore not surprising that some of the notes in Manuscript K1 are duplicates: rapid notes that once in the calm of his studio, he further developed. The Codex 'On the Flight of Birds' (with a format slightly larger than the others) dates from this period and is the rare example of a manuscript by Leonardo dedicated (almost) exclusively to a single topic: flight, both in its natural form and the imitation of natural flight with the flying machine. Now more than ever, the project for the flying machine becomes an attempt at the radical imitation of nature, the bird in nature, in all its forms and actions. This can be immediately observed upon analysing the Codex 'On the Flight of Birds', which consists of two main sections: one centred primarily on flapping flight or active flight (propulsion obtained by the beating of wings), and the other, dealing with in-flight equilibrium manoeuvres in the presence of wind. It is interesting that each section is composed of two types of study: naturalistic studies relative to flight techniques in birds, having as it basis the laws of anatomy and aerodynamics, and, mechanical studies where Leonardo attempts to perfect a model of the flying machine capable of imitating what he observed in nature. It is important to underline how strongly Leonardo believed in the possibility that man could imitate the flight of birds. His confidence derives from his general conception of the world of nature, so important to him during these years. He is convinced that there is a profound analogy between all living beings. In his studies on comparative anatomy he attempts to demonstrate a series of similarities between man and other animals, for example, four-legged animals. In fact, Leonardo notes that when man is a baby, he too, walks on four legs. As he grows, the dynamic relationship in man's carriage between the upper and lower limbs is analogous to the fore and hind legs of the quadrupeds. Leonardo's conviction regarding the possibility of human flight is founded on this general analogy between man and animals.

Even later, Leonardo continues to believe in active human flight resulting from the force generated in his muscles. Nonetheless, during this final phase in his life, while on one hand aerostatic-type of flight is given greater space in his thoughts (the famous study of the descent of man attached to a plank in Manuscript G, f. 74r), on the other, there is a decline in mechanical projects and an increase in studies dedicated purely to theory (many of which are contained in Manuscript E). During this period, even the flight acrobatics of birds are studied not so much for research on the flying machine, but for indirectly studying the laws behind air currents and wind. Even in this phase, however, mention of artificial flight is not totally lacking. The traditional sources (Vasari, Lomazzo) relate very different outcomes about Leonardo's research. For example, Leonardo dedicates himself to making birds and other flying objects using automatic mechanisms or by inflating elastic materials. An epilogue of pastimes, of amusements. A destiny that will touch other aspects of Leonardo's research into mechanics.

Vinci, 1452

1460

1470

1480-1485

1490

1500

1510

Amboise, 1519

Codex Atlanticus, f. 1051v

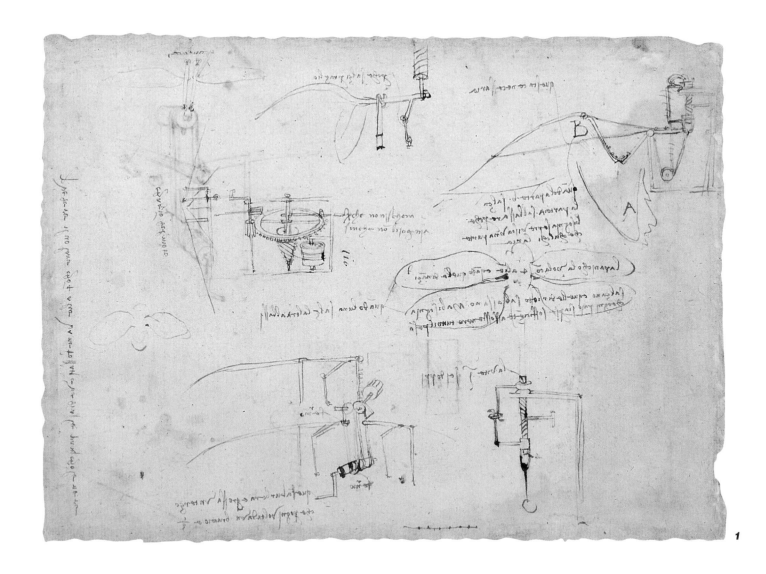

1

Mechanisms
for Mechanical Wings

Leonardo worked on this folio from the Codex Atlanticus when he was about thirty years old, during the time he was still in Florence or immediately after leaving for Milan in 1482. There are two reasons that it is interesting. On one hand it is a typical work sheet, and on the other, it is one of the oldest examples demonstrating the link between a flying machine and studies on natural flight. It represents one of the most original aspects of Leonardo's research in this area, and perhaps even the most fascinating.

Leonardo left precious autobiographical testimony in his writings. His manuscripts are like a personal diary, not of day-to-day events, but events tied to his work, his scientific or artistic research. He uses his written notes, and especially his drawings, to systematically record every movement of his thoughts on a given problem. Thus, by analysing the page with its notes and drawings, the concrete development of his research, observations, doubts, work projects and so forth can be reconstructed.

We can not identify with any certainty the succession of his notes and thoughts on the page. Perhaps the dragonfly (on the right) and the other flying insect (on the left) were among the first of the drawings In both cases, they are barely more than quick sketches. Certainly, Leonardo did not intend to portray these small animals in full detail, but to simply fix an impression, a thought, referred to in the written note that he makes over the main drawing. By observing the flight of these insects, Leonardo deduced that when the front pair of wings go up (preparing for a downstroke), the back pair go down, ensuring a surface for support on the air. Thus, we have a first group of notes and drawings on the study of natural flight.

On the other hand, there is different group of drawing and notes that addresses mechanical flight. Specifically, the drawing in the upper left of the page represents a mechanical wing comprised of two sections, an inner section (A), and an outer section (B). During the wing beat, when the outer section goes up, the inner section remains lowered on the air supporting the machine in flight. The mechanism of this artificial wing results, therefore, from an imitation of what is observed in natural flight.

A long note along the left margin of the page is testimony to another phase in Leonardo's research. As often occurs on Leonardo's pages, it deals with a work project: 'To see four-winged flight, go around the ditches and you will see the black net-wings'. We can not say if Leonardo meant to further develop the zoological observations already made and noted on this page, or if these are the fruit of planned recognisance.

fig. 1
In the centre of the page there is the faint drawing of a dragonfly, while surrounding it Leonardo draws mechanisms that attempt to mechanically reproduce movements for flight.

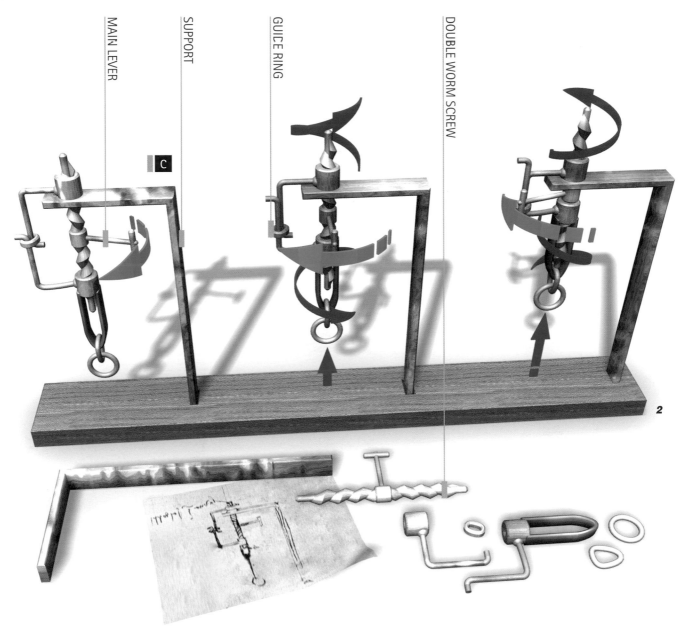

MAIN LEVER

SUPPORT

GUICE RING

DOUBLE WORM SCREW

A
B
Leonardo himself clearly describes the workings of the device, and uses the letters A and B to indicate the points where the mechanical wing should flex. The wing function on this machine serves to fold a mechanical wing. By activating the motor mechanism, point A should lower while point B moves in the opposite direction. The sum of these movements will give a wing motion very similar to that found in animals.

C
In the study model for the mechanical wing the fundamental part is the propulsory mechanism. It is a complex instrument, and even while he is designing it Leonardo changes his mind. This is seen in the sketch in the upper right (fig. 1) where he crosses out a technical solution that he considered to be wrong. In the final configuration the mechanism has a double worm screw that puts the entire wing in movement by activating a small lever.

D
The final movement of the wing generated by the continual motion of the lever imitates nature: in fact, the wing behaves much like the wing beat of an animal where the extremities complete a longer and different trajectory than the wing near the body, almost closing up on itself.

fig. 2
Workings of the drive motor.

fig. 3
Automatic system for folding in the mechanical wing. An operator works the lever putting the mechanisms in motion; in turn these produce the motion and rotation of the wing supports.

fig. 4
A dynamic sequence of the motion.

STUDY MODEL FOR THE MECHANICAL WING

DRAGONFLY USED FOR REFERENCE

DRIVE MECHANISM

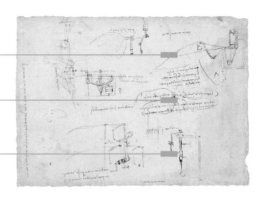

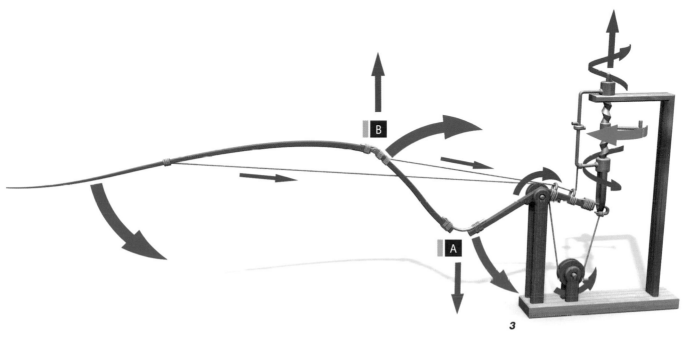

3

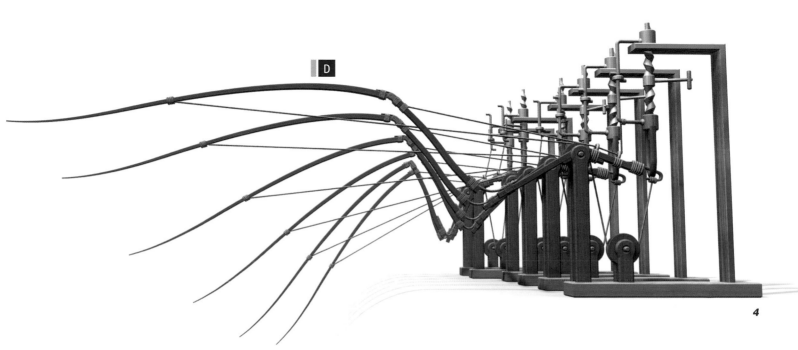

4

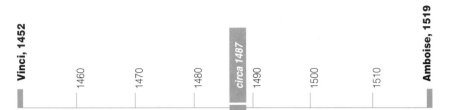

1460 1470 1480 *circa 1487* 1490 1500 1510

Ashburnham I, f. 10v

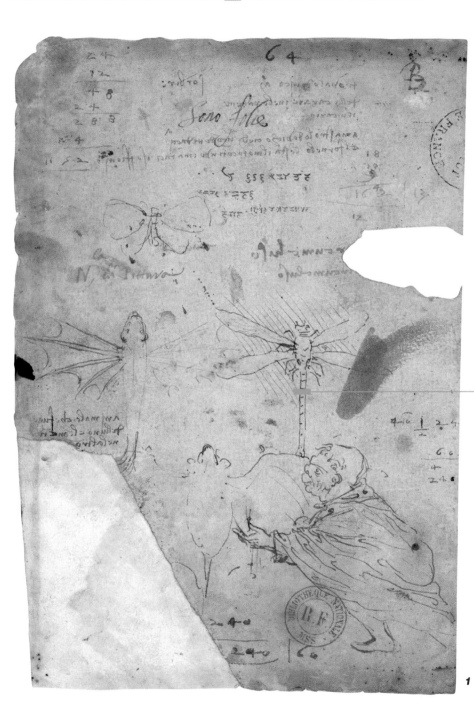

1

Dragonfly

The manuscript today known as Ashburnham I was originally part of Manuscript B. In the nineteenth century it was stolen from the latter, but was later recovered. Thus, the drawings and notes on this page date from the time Manuscript B was being compiled; it is about 1485-1490, and Leonardo is in Milan.

During this period, Leonardo is pursuing two main paths in his research on human flight: studies on the fundamental laws of natural flight and its imitation; studies on the dynamic potentialities of the human body and the elaboration of the mechanisms able to use this potentiality to the fullest. This latter branch of his research seemed prevalent, but it never overrides the fundamental idea behind the flying machine: the imitation of the flight of winged creatures. Some of the studies on this folio deal with flight as found in nature. Here, Leonardo depicted various airborne creatures: a flying fish, a bat, a dragonfly (or in a different interpretation, an ant-lion, a winged-insect similar to a dragonfly), and another flying insect. On one level it is a study of animals; on a more specific level it is a comparative study of the morphology of various animals seen from the perspective of Aristotelian biology, a vantage point to which Leonardo will remain faithful until the end. Leonardo compares four-winged flying animals with animals having membrane-covered wings. He is interested in the differences, but above all in the similarities. He demonstrates this by including and giving particular attention to the flying fish, and as he specifies in a note, it is an animal that is capable of flitting through both air and water. Through this analogy Leonardo studies water and its whirlpools in order to grasp the laws underlying the behaviour of an invisible element such as air. The flying fish was almost the incarnation of the basic analogy of the animals, humans included, in the various elements. In Leonardo's eyes this analogy is the foundation for the possibility of human flight.

The comparative zoological studies are thus connected to those on the flying machine. The types of mechanical wings Leonardo designed during this period, many of which are in Manuscript B, are in fact double wings (as seen in two of the animals depicted on the page) or membrane-covered wings, in imitation of the bat or flying fish.

fig. 1
The folio from the Codex Ashburnham I, originally part of Manuscript B.

fig. 2
Three-dimensional reconstruction of a dragonfly in the centre of the page in a sketch by Leonardo.

overleaf, following page, fig. 3
A hypothetical reconstruction of the way Manuscript B, a notebook containing 100 pages, may have looked when Leonardo began it. This folio was later removed from the original manuscript. Part of the drawings in this volume are dedicated to mechanical flight, and also take their inspiration from this first dragonfly.

Vinci, 1452

1460

1470

1480

1487-1489

1490

1500

1510

Amboise, 1519

Manuscript B, f. 88v

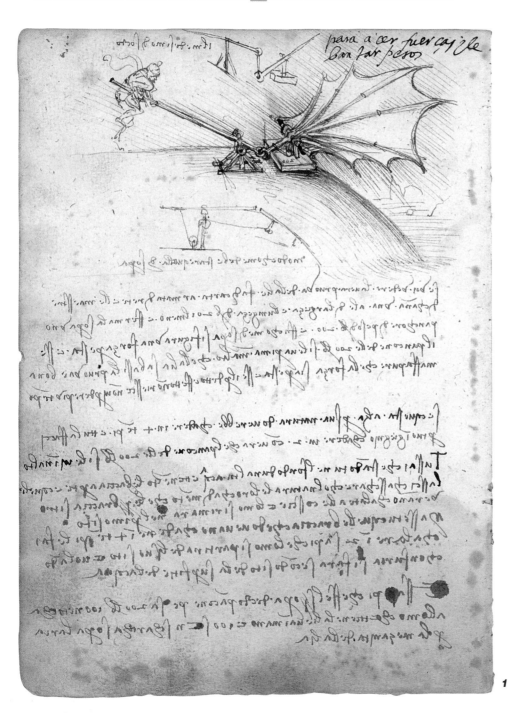

1

Flapping Wing

Leonardo conceives of the flying machine, especially in a first phase, as a dynamic challenge that man hurls against nature. Leonardo reasons that air, unlike water, can be compressed. Man could keep himself in flight with the artificial wing of the machine compressing the air, just as if he were navigating on water. The problem consists in flapping the wing with sufficient speed to prevent the compressed air from escaping into the surrounding air. The problem of the speed was a question of dynamics, of adequate force being generated by man. The project on this folio of Manuscript B is meant to test the capacity of the human body and a wing of a given amplitude in raising a board weighing two hundred Florentine *libbre* (about 68 kilograms). It is the plan for an actual experiment to be undertaken on a hillside, which Leonardo indeed could have carried out. Leonardo expresses the empirical dimension of this study through a very complete drawing, containing indications not only on the machine and how it works, but also on the type of landscape necessary for the experiment. He uses the tools common to every machinist between the Middle Ages and Renaissance: a notebook and pen. The pen, however, is not limited to only jotting down notes or a rapid visual diagram. It is used to create a remarkably complex drawing, even if only in the form of a notation. The image was made first; the text underneath is a caption added later, a further explanation. In addition to presenting the morphology of the mechanism under experimentation, the drawing also shows its dynamics: the lever activated by a man is in a raised position. The hatching around the external limits of the wing seems to reproduce the variable curvilinear profile of the wing, almost visualising the quivering part of the compressed air. Before he carries out his experiment, Leonardo rehearses it in his visual and graphic imagination. Although it is not the case here, the force of Leonardo's drawing at times is such that the project does not need, nor was it meant, to be physically carried out. On the board, we can see the figure '200', the weight to be used (200 *libbre*). On the right there is the slope of a hill, a few quickly drawn landscape elements (a mountain and a slope showing the opposite valley, a building in the distance). It is possible that Leonardo had a specific site in mind. Above and below the main drawing there are studies for devices correlated to it. On the upper right a written note was inserted at a later date and is not by Leonardo.

fig. 1
Project for a flapping wing on folio 88v from Manuscript B; the folio contains the main drawing and the notations on the project, but there are also two important ideas for eventual modifications.

fig. 2
Side view of the project for the articulated version of the experiment for the flapping wing.

2

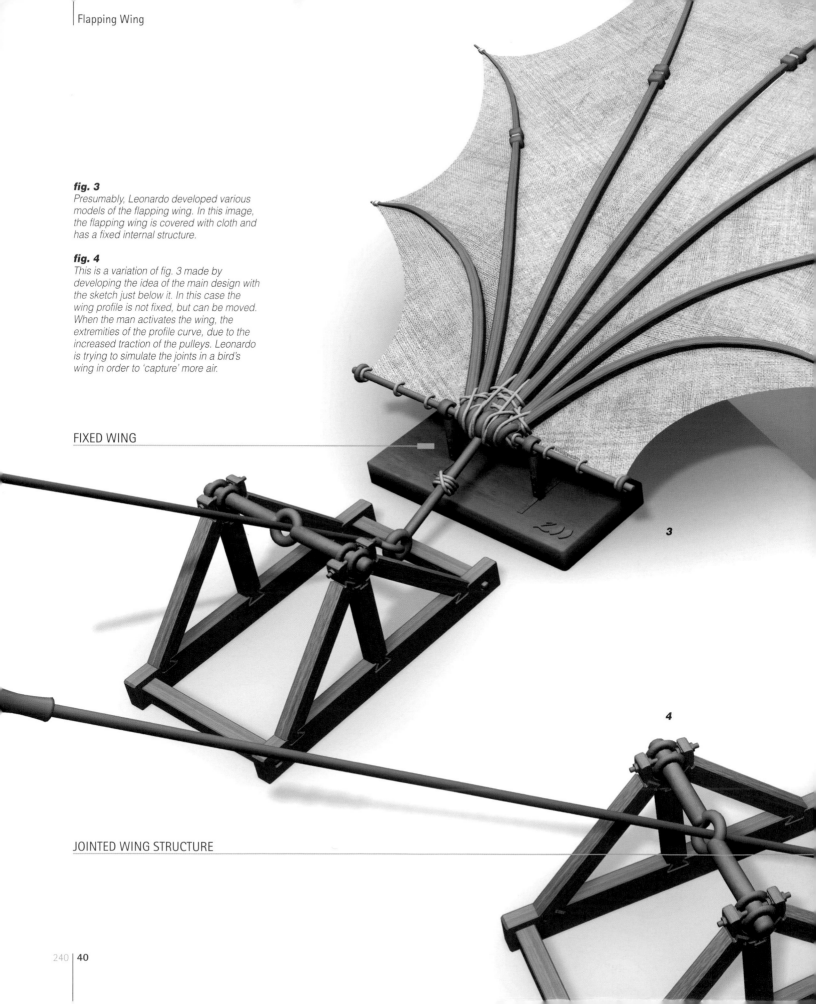

fig. 3
Presumably, Leonardo developed various
models of the flapping wing. In this image,
the flapping wing is covered with cloth and
has a fixed internal structure.

fig. 4
This is a variation of fig. 3 made by
developing the idea of the main design with
the sketch just below it. In this case the
wing profile is not fixed, but can be moved.
When the man activates the wing, the
extremities of the profile curve, due to the
increased traction of the pulleys. Leonardo
is trying to simulate the joints in a bird's
wing in order to 'capture' more air.

FIXED WING

JOINTED WING STRUCTURE

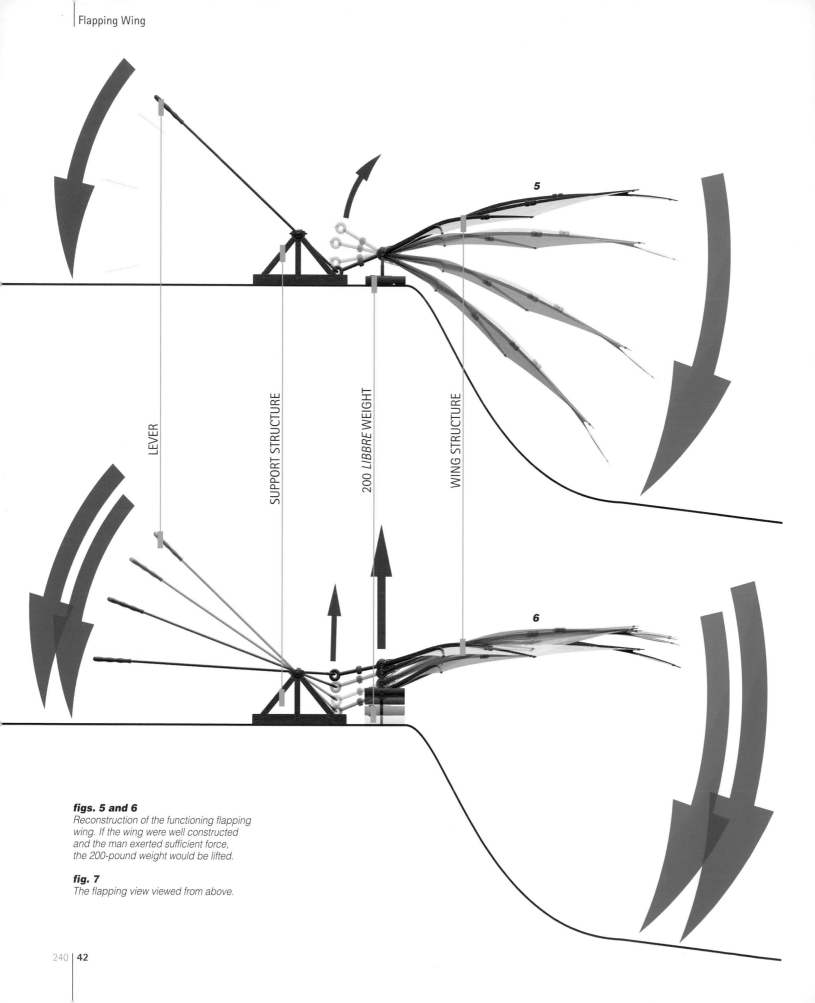

5

6

LEVER

SUPPORT STRUCTURE

200 *LIBBRE* WEIGHT

WING STRUCTURE

figs. 5 and 6
*Reconstruction of the functioning flapping
wing. If the wing were well constructed
and the man exerted sufficient force,
the 200-pound weight would be lifted.*

fig. 7
The flapping view viewed from above.

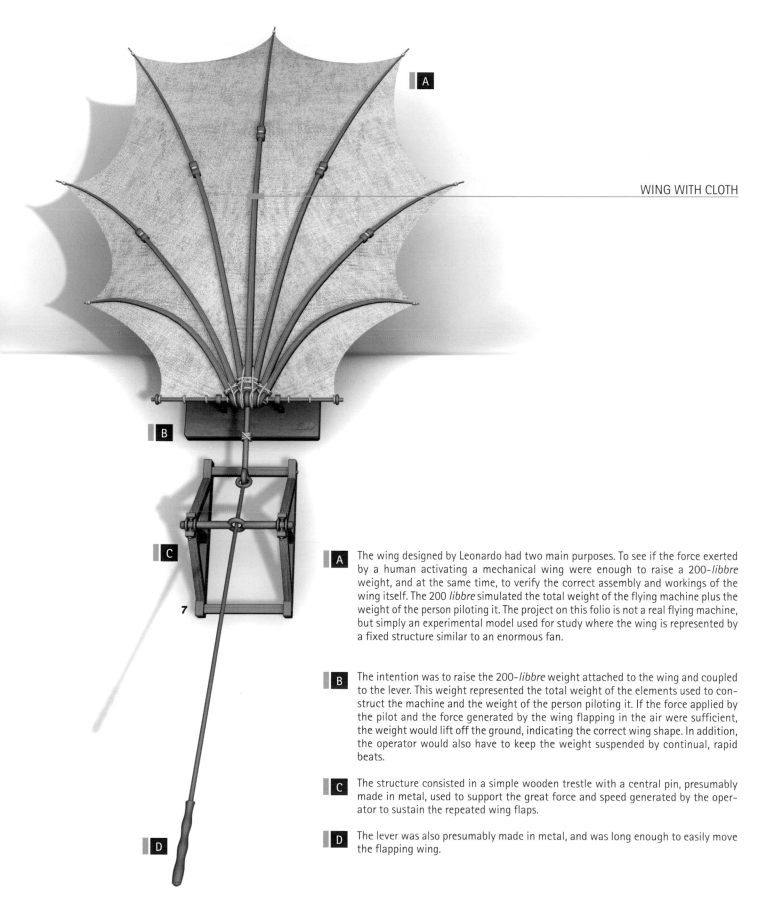

WING WITH CLOTH

7

A The wing designed by Leonardo had two main purposes. To see if the force exerted by a human activating a mechanical wing were enough to raise a 200-*libbre* weight, and at the same time, to verify the correct assembly and workings of the wing itself. The 200 *libbre* simulated the total weight of the flying machine plus the weight of the person piloting it. The project on this folio is not a real flying machine, but simply an experimental model used for study where the wing is represented by a fixed structure similar to an enormous fan.

B The intention was to raise the 200-*libbre* weight attached to the wing and coupled to the lever. This weight represented the total weight of the elements used to construct the machine and the weight of the person piloting it. If the force applied by the pilot and the force generated by the wing flapping in the air were sufficient, the weight would lift off the ground, indicating the correct wing shape. In addition, the operator would also have to keep the weight suspended by continual, rapid beats.

C The structure consisted in a simple wooden trestle with a central pin, presumably made in metal, used to support the great force and speed generated by the operator to sustain the repeated wing flaps.

D The lever was also presumably made in metal, and was long enough to easily move the flapping wing.

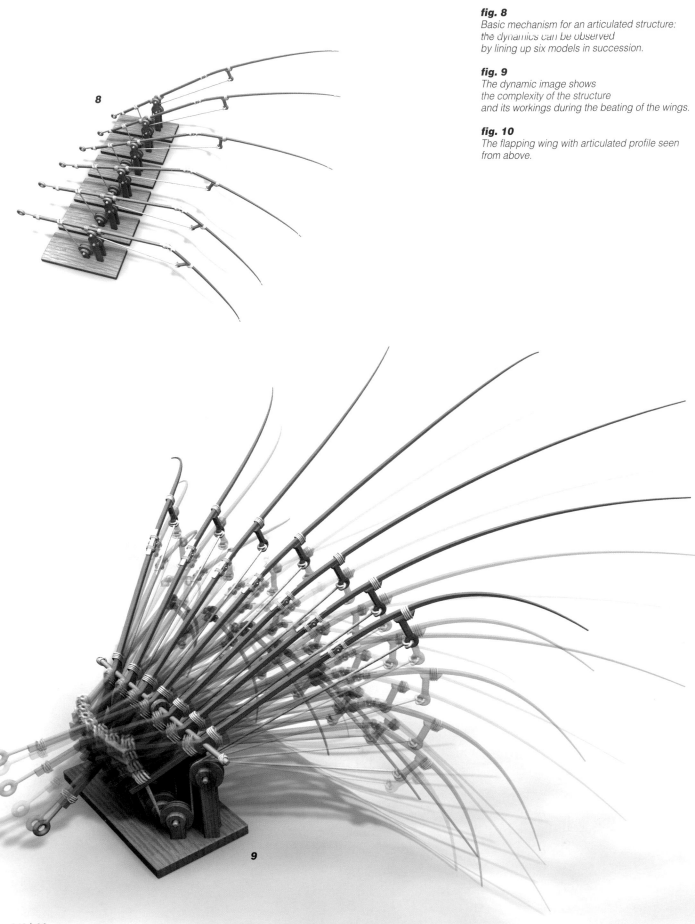

fig. 8
Basic mechanism for an articulated structure:
the dynamics can be observed
by lining up six models in succession.

fig. 9
The dynamic image shows
the complexity of the structure
and its workings during the beating of the wings.

fig. 10
The flapping wing with articulated profile seen
from above.

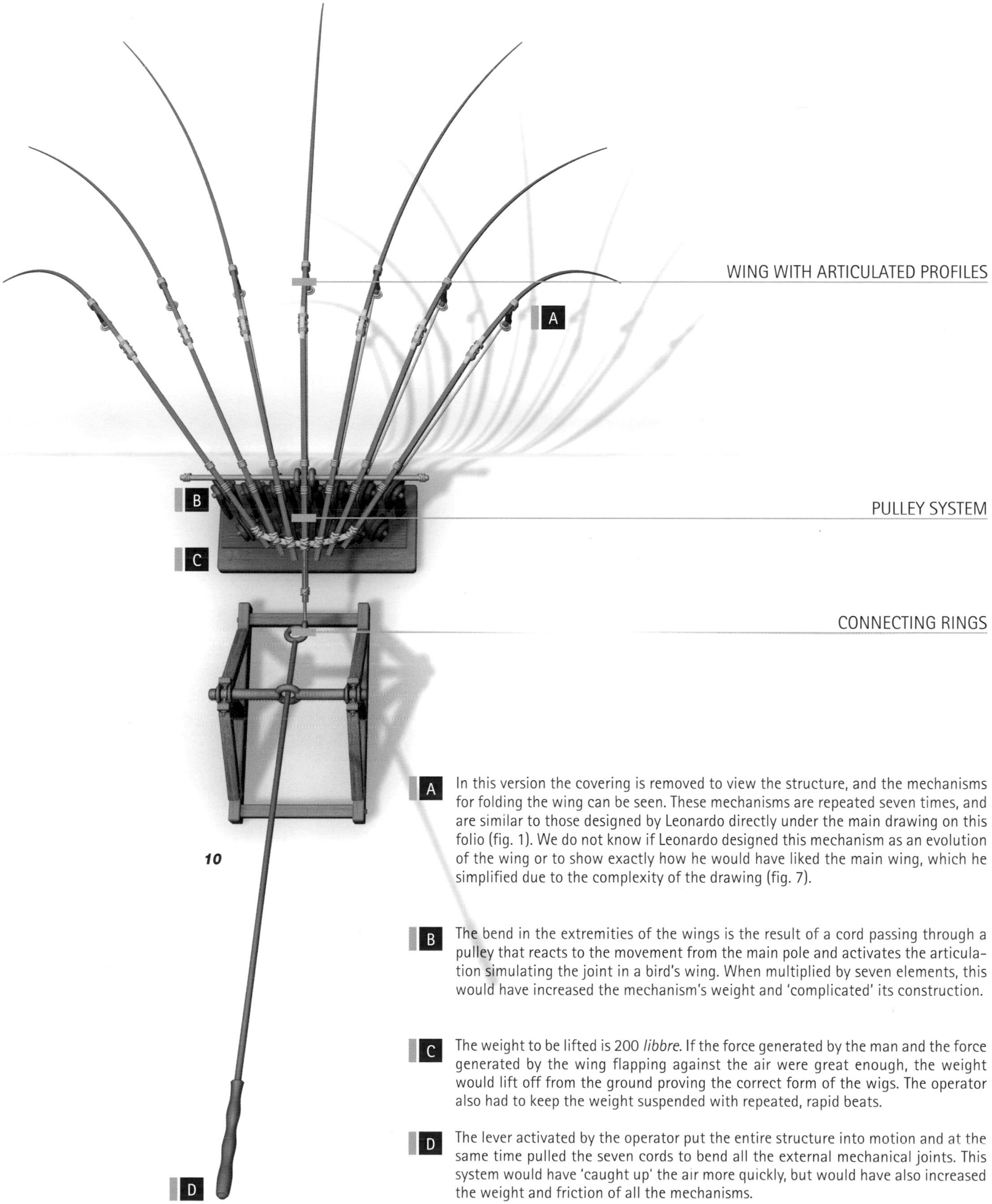

WING WITH ARTICULATED PROFILES

A

PULLEY SYSTEM

B

C

CONNECTING RINGS

10

A In this version the covering is removed to view the structure, and the mechanisms for folding the wing can be seen. These mechanisms are repeated seven times, and are similar to those designed by Leonardo directly under the main drawing on this folio (fig. 1). We do not know if Leonardo designed this mechanism as an evolution of the wing or to show exactly how he would have liked the main wing, which he simplified due to the complexity of the drawing (fig. 7).

B The bend in the extremities of the wings is the result of a cord passing through a pulley that reacts to the movement from the main pole and activates the articulation simulating the joint in a bird's wing. When multiplied by seven elements, this would have increased the mechanism's weight and 'complicated' its construction.

C The weight to be lifted is 200 *libbre*. If the force generated by the man and the force generated by the wing flapping against the air were great enough, the weight would lift off from the ground proving the correct form of the wigs. The operator also had to keep the weight suspended with repeated, rapid beats.

D The lever activated by the operator put the entire structure into motion and at the same time pulled the seven cords to bend all the external mechanical joints. This system would have 'caught up' the air more quickly, but would have also increased the weight and friction of all the mechanisms.

D

Vinci, 1452

1460

1470

1480

circa 1489

1490

1500

1510

Amboise, 1519

Manuscript B, f. 83v

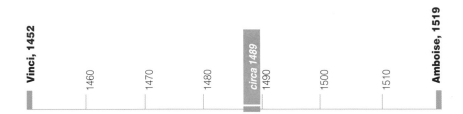

1

Aerial Screw

This study for an aerial screw appears in one of the folios from Manuscript B, alongside other flying machines. It is a device that when rotated is supposed to lift off in flight. Even this drawing, like the others in this codex, is made with pen and ink, a technique that allows for rapid, accurate execution. With his eye towards human flight, Leonardo dedicates much of his attention to the dynamic potentialities of the human body (the driving force behind the flying machine), as well as to another aspect of the problem: the air, the element in which the flying machine had to operate. The idea of an aerial screw is conceived in this context of his scientific studies. This is an important step. Putting aside the theoretical and scientific dimension of this project for the moment, in the best of hypotheses it appears to be only a utopian anticipation of modern advances. Leonardo studies the air, and he reaches the conclusion that unlike water, it can be compressed if enough energy is exerted upon it. One of the most extraordinary studies in Manuscript B (folio 88v) is the notation on an experiment verifying this action. The aerial screw develops from the very same order of ideas. The hatched areas around the machine, just as for the experimental wing on folio 88v, very effectively render the tangible, even though invisible, presence of the air. If air can be compressed, then it follows that it has material density. Based on this conclusion, Leonardo believes that a device in the form of a screw, rotating very quickly, can lift itself up in flight. This device will bore into the fluid density of the air just as a screw does into other materials. The possibility of achieving this movement was obviously based on sufficient rotating speed. Thus, in the final analysis, the problem was tied to another area under investigation: how to obtain adequate force.

As often occurs in Leonardo's projects, this aspect of the problem is not fully developed. It is not completely clear if the screw would be rotated by men or by a line quickly unwound, like a spinning top. Conversely, Leonardo deals only with generating force in his amazing project for the flying ship (folio 80r in Manuscript B).

As usual, our impression is that rather than following a systematic path in designing a machine capable of flight, Leonardo investigates different theoretical problems such as man's dynamic potential, the physical characteristics of air, etc. Within the realm of each area he investigates, he elaborates a project for a machine where he can 'visualise' his theoretical conclusions. The spiral form has been omnipresent in the field of hydraulics (the hydraulic systems based on the Archimedean screw, or the worm screw come to mind), but it should be noted that this case is the first time that a spiral form is applied to flight and air.

fig. 1
The central portion of folio 83v in Manuscript B shows the project for the aerial screw along with notes on its construction.

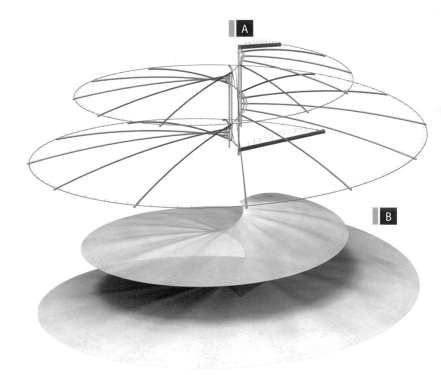

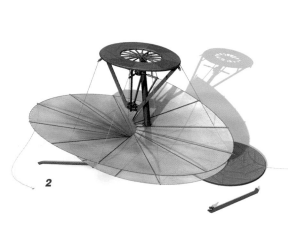

fig. 2
The inevitable result of Leonardo's helicopter. In fact, the project for the aerial screw is notoriously called Leonardo's helicopter. In reality, given its structural and constructive characteristics, it would not have functioned correctly, nor would it have made use of the dynamic principles of the modern-day helicopter. One only needs to turn back three pages in Manuscript B to find something more technically similar to a machine that flies like a helicopter.

fig. 3
Exploded view of the aerial screw, with dismantled elements and connections.

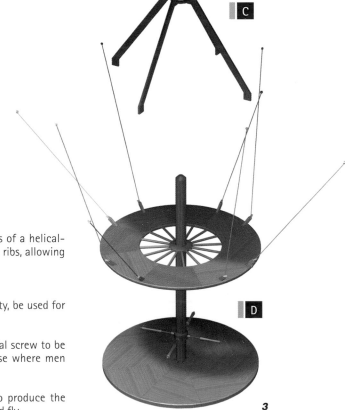

A The flying structure conceived for the aerial screw project consists of a helical-shaped iron stay attached to a central mast with a series of wooden ribs, allowing the 'wing' to be covered in cloth and fixed to the main structure.

B Leonardo suggests that linen, sized with starch to reduce its porosity, be used for covering the helical structure.

C A system of wooden trestles allows the 'wing' structure of the aerial screw to be attached to the central mast and consequently the operating base where men would work the rotating mechanism.

D The circular, wooden operating platform houses the men used to produce the energy necessary for the screw to bore into the density of the air and fly.

BLOCK A – FLYING STRUCTURE

BLOCK B – PILOTING DECK

figs. 4 and 5
*The images show the aerial screw sitting
on the manuscript page as if it were a mock-up
in paper and wood suggested by Leonardo.
Helical structure covered
with cloth (fig. 5) and the version
without covering (fig. 4)*

CLOTH COVERING

HELICAL STRUCTURE

OPERATING PLATFORM

4

5

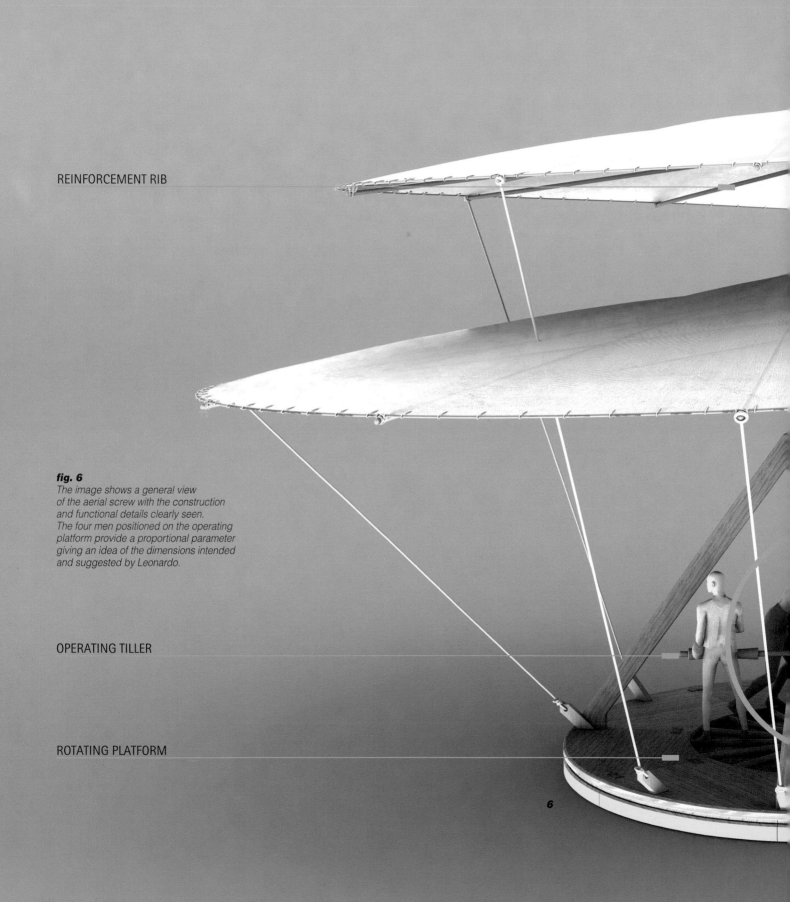

REINFORCEMENT RIB

fig. 6
*The image shows a general view
of the aerial screw with the construction
and functional details clearly seen.
The four men positioned on the operating
platform provide a proportional parameter
giving an idea of the dimensions intended
and suggested by Leonardo.*

OPERATING TILLER

ROTATING PLATFORM

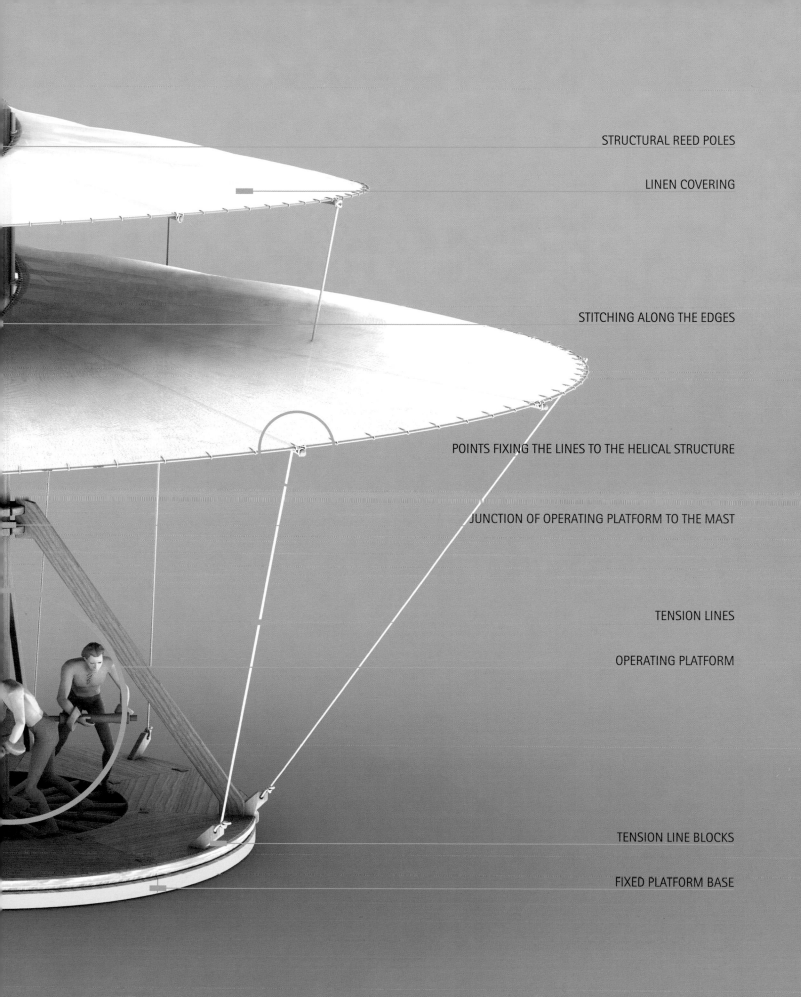

STRUCTURAL REED POLES

LINEN COVERING

STITCHING ALONG THE EDGES

POINTS FIXING THE LINES TO THE HELICAL STRUCTURE

JUNCTION OF OPERATING PLATFORM TO THE MAST

TENSION LINES

OPERATING PLATFORM

TENSION LINE BLOCKS

FIXED PLATFORM BASE

E In the note Leonardo makes for himself, he suggests that the helical structure should be made with thick iron wire, and also indicates that the diameter should be 8 *braccia* (1 *braccio* is about 58 centimetres, or 2 feet).

F In the notes on the page, he indicates that a linen cloth should be used to cover the structure and that it should be sized with starch to close the pores. In order to lighten the structure he suggests long, sturdy reed canes. Finally, he notes (perhaps to himself) that a small paper mock-up should be made in order to study the functional aspects.

fig. 7
The folio with two types of annotations: lateral dimensions (E), constructional dimensions below (F).

fig. 8
Technical image of the aerial screw, showing the morphological complexity and elegance of design.

8

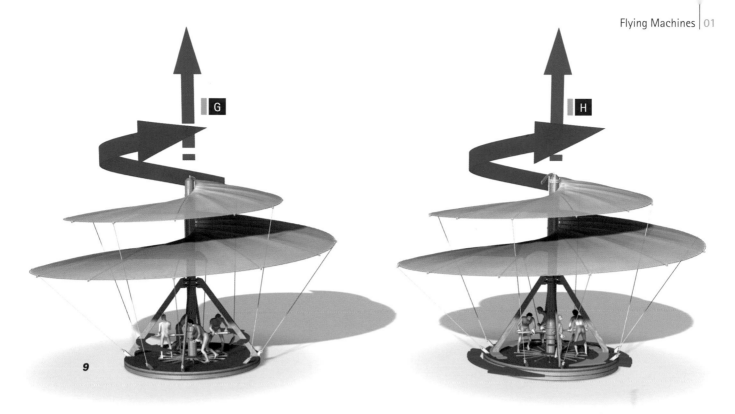

G Four men grasp the four poles on the operating tiller. They remain stationary while they push with their feet against the structure (red arrow) firmly attached to the propeller. Thus, the propeller begins to move and once a hypothetical 'boring' of the air is achieved the main structure and the rotating platform lift up, leaving the men and the central mooring used as a starter to direct the rotation on the ground.

H In the second hypothesis, the structures are placed differently. The four men are part of the flying 'vehicle', and by pushing with their feet they begin to turn like a merry-go-round on the playground (red arrow). When the screw turns fast enough to bore into the air (clockwise), theoretically the structure should begin to fly. The base against which the men push, however, would begin to turn in the opposite direction. Thus, even if the structure were initially pushed upwards, it would not be able to fly because there would be nothing for the feet to push against and the two opposite rotations would clash.

In whatever case and combination, the final result would certainly be as depicted in fig. 2. The modern helicopter solves the problem of rotational stability by using a small propeller on the end of the tail that prevents it from circling around on itself. Additionally, its principle of flight is based on aerodynamic lift rather than boring through the air as Leonardo had imagined.

figs. 9 and 10
These images show two different hypotheses for working the machine. In both cases the helical canvas is made to turn in a clockwise (when view from above) direction, boring itself into the air just as Leonardo describes. The rotary motion could be generated in two ways.

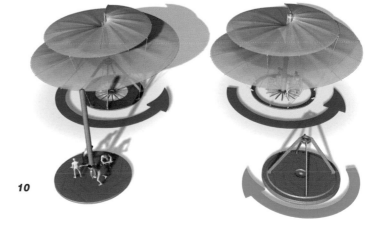

Vinci, 1452

1460

1470

1480

1488-1489

1490

1500

1510

Amboise, 1519

Manuscript B, f. 74v

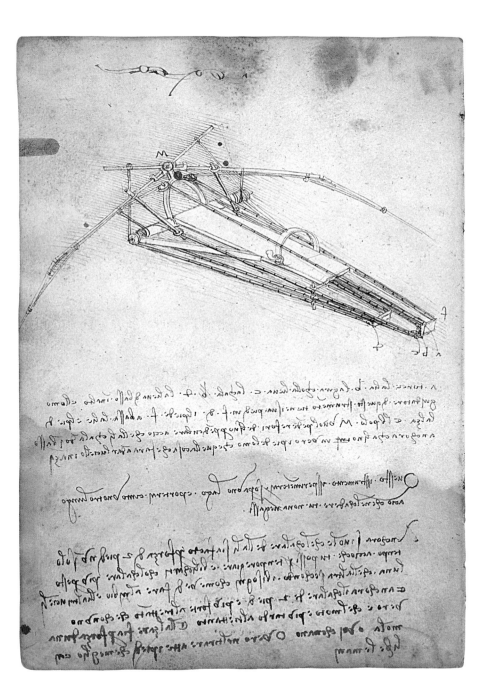

1

Flying Machine

2

The drawing on this page of Manuscript B and the three notes written underneath make up a very complex unit. In fact, all the notations refer to the machine in the drawing. This impression of organic unity is furthered by the style of the drawing and the note right under it. The drawing is highly finished and delineated by a very precise, clean line while the layout of the written note is very regular. These are both aspects typical to the years around the 1490s when Leonardo reaches a remarkable intellectual equilibrium, which, in a certain sense, is manifested in his graphic style. It must be stated, however, that it is not something that happens effortlessly. Even if the impression is one of a well-organised page, fundamentally it is still a working note made for himself. The different writing styles contribute to this statement. Initially, Leonardo makes the drawing and writes the first note underneath it. In a later phase, he goes back to the page and inserts the other two notes. This is almost always Leonardo's way of working. For him, the sheet of paper is like a painting; he continues to apply his 'brushstrokes', sometimes in the form of notes, other times as drawings, as long as there is empty space on the 'canvas'.

Just as in other projects taken up during this period, Leonardo attempts to combine the dynamic potentialities of the human body in the in the best possible way. This type of research is fundamental for Leonardo in this period and it generates a series of projects for the flying machine where the pilot is standing straight up. Contemporarily, however, he does not lose sight of the theme dealing with the imitation of natural flight, especially evident in the group of projects we are looking at where the pilot is in a horizontal position. His notes clearly reveal this mimetic concept: Leonardo cites the kite and other birds as models to imitate, and even at one point mentions the flying machine referring to it as a 'bird'. Nature and technology overlap in his mind. This concept will be even more evident later on in Leonardo, during the period of the Codex 'On the Flight of Birds'.

One of the three notes is about an experiment to be carried out using the flying machine. Leonardo plans to use the machine on a lake, in order to reduce the risks from a fall.

fig. 1
The image on the folio 74v of Manuscript B puts the project for the flying machine in a central position.

fig. 2
Model of the flying machine placed on top of a reconstruction of Manuscript B, opened to folio 74v.

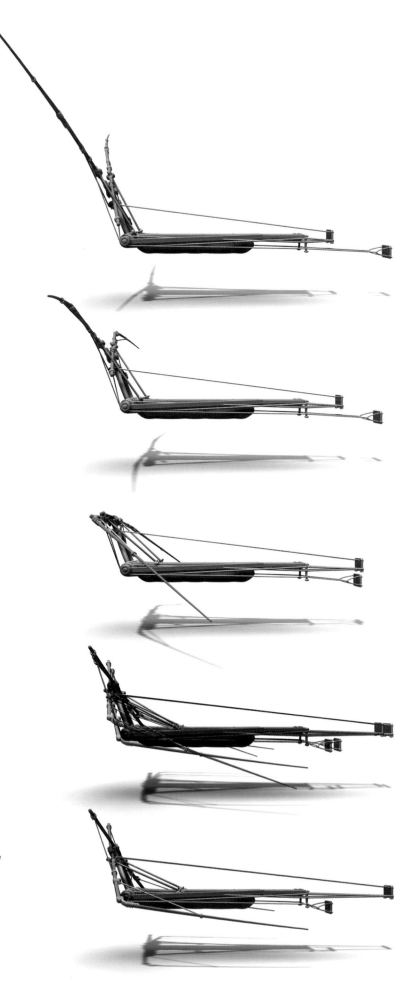

figs. 3 and 4
*The sequence of images, seen from the side
(fig. 3) and front (fig. 4), shows the development
and the dynamics of the workings of the flying
machine.
The sequence, from top to bottom, synthesises
the folding in of the wings. Going from bottom
to top, the wings open.
Each frame in the series helps to understand the
type of movements made by the machine and the
components of each movement. The image is
indicative of the complexity of the fundamental
working principle in this Da Vincian project.*

3

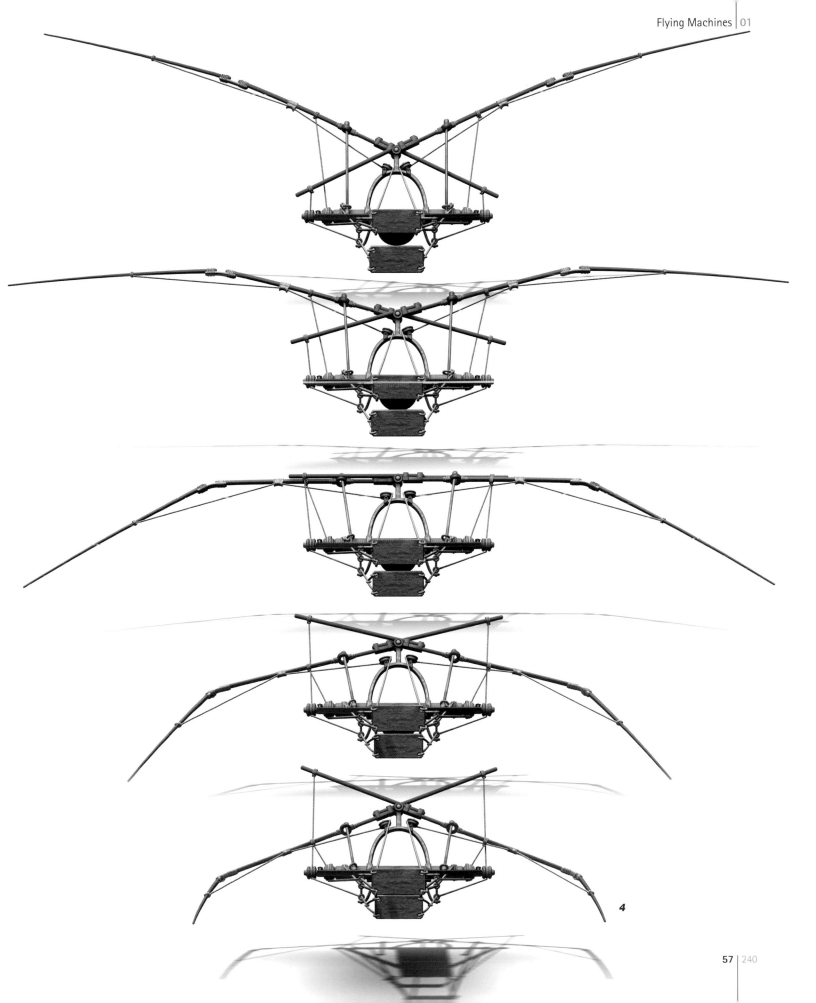

4

MAIN JOINT

AREA FOR THE PILOT

FLOTATION DEVICE

MAIN PEDAL FOR CLOSING WINGS

RELEASE PEDAL - OPEN WINGS

fig. 5
*This image shows the main components of the
flying machine, seen from underneath.*

fig. 6
*The dynamic sequence in six steps
(digitally superimposed) of the wing movement
can be seen in this image.
It should be noted that, in addition to completing
a rotatory movement, when the wings bend they
make a flexing movement towards the interior.
The result is a compound motion that totally
imitates bird flight.*

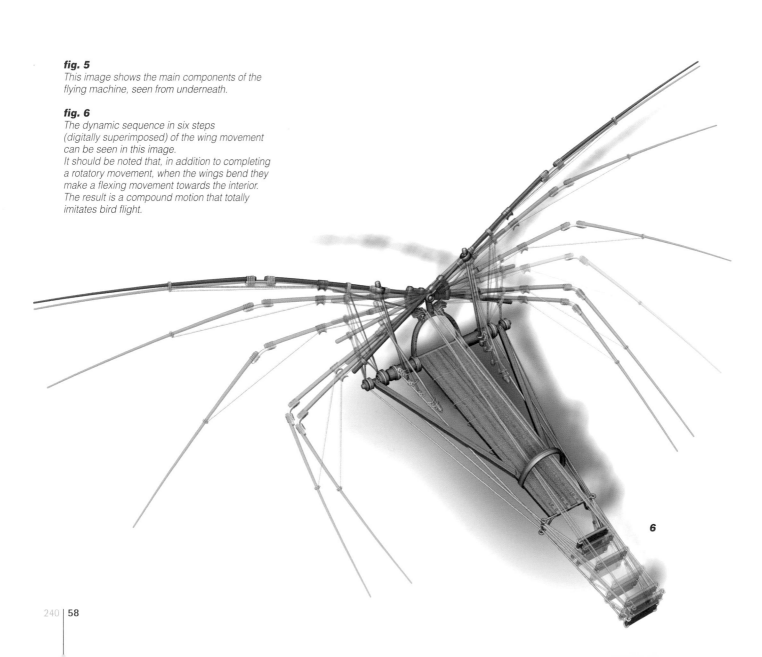

fig. 7
This hypothetical flight test includes
the addition of a wing structure,
very similar to what Leonardo designed
on the reverse of the same folio
with the design for this flying machine
(74r in Manuscript B).

For safety reasons, Leonardo believes
that this machine should be tested over a lake,
placing the flotation device on the underside to
keep it from sinking if it falls in water.

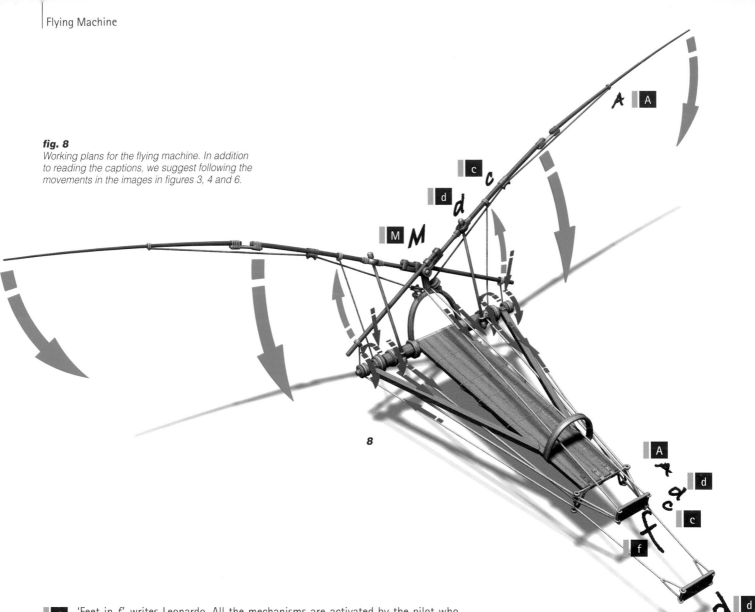

fig. 8
Working plans for the flying machine. In addition to reading the captions, we suggest following the movements in the images in figures 3, 4 and 6.

f 'Feet in *f*', writes Leonardo. All the mechanisms are activated by the pilot who pushes with both feet against pedal f. This pulls three different cords, which Leonardo refers to as a, b, c.

A '*A* twists the wing'. Line *A* passing through a pulley system is connected to the extremity of the wing. The wing tip folds when it is pulled.

b '*b* turns it with a lever'. Line *b* runs through a metal ring that moves the bar attached to the wing giving it a rotatory motion.

c '*c* lowers it'. Line *c* by using a system of pulleys produces the main up-down flapping movement in the wings.

M 'The pivot *M* should have its centre of gravity just off the perpendicular so that as the wings fall they also fall towards the man's feet'. The metal structure supporting pivot *M* is bet forward to allow for the correct movement in the wings.

d 'the foot *d* raises the wings...*d* moves from bottom to top'. Once the wings are spread using pedal *f*, the pilot re-opens the wings by pushing the other pedal, pedal *d*. Leonardo suggests that this movement can be helped by the use of a series of springs.

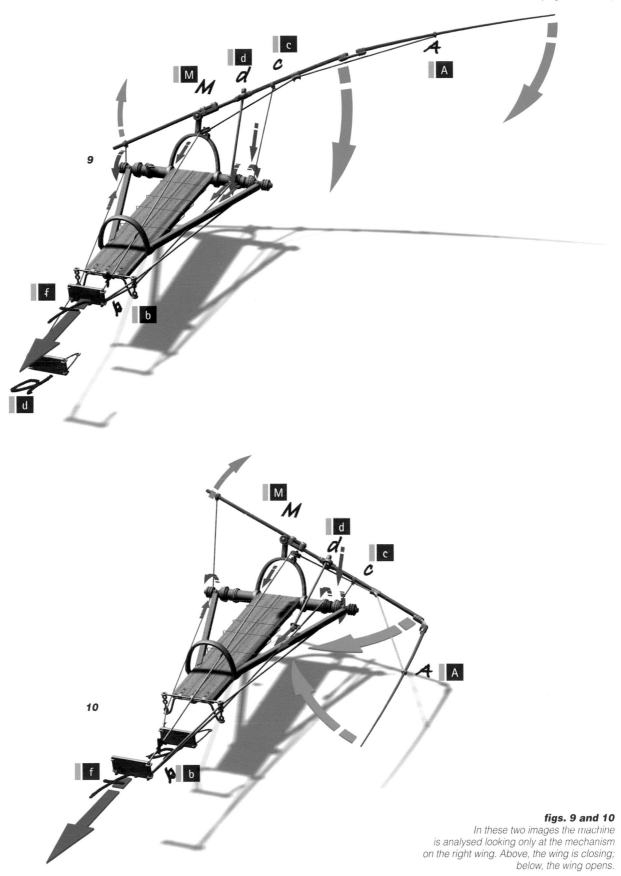

figs. 9 and 10
*In these two images the machine
is analysed looking only at the mechanism
on the right wing. Above, the wing is closing;
below, the wing opens.*

Vinci, 1452

1460

1470

1480

1490

1493-1495

1500

1510

Amboise, 1519

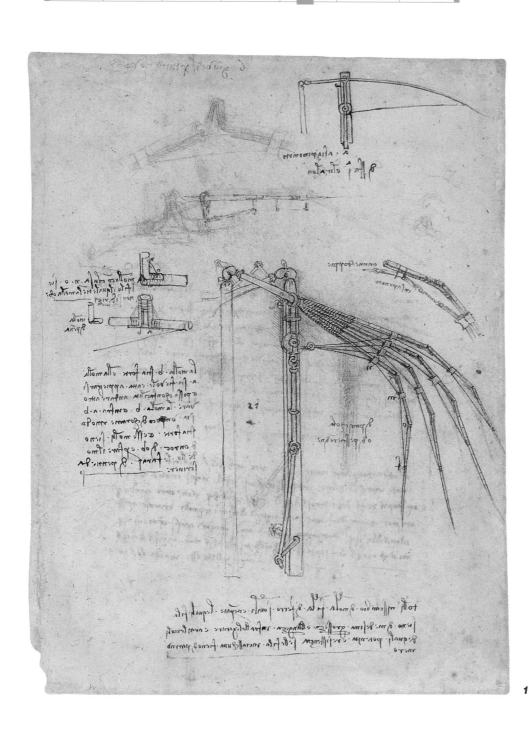

1

Mechanical Wings

2

This folio was made in Milan around 1494. It is more than just a work sheet with a few hasty notes. The project on this page for a mechanical wing is very mature in character. It is the point of arrival and the synthesis of a series of studies. Here, Leonardo meant to realise a fairly complete and finished drawing. We know this not only from the intrinsic contents of the project, rich with details on the functioning of the wing and its various parts, but also from the style of the drawing itself. Except for the small drawing in the upper right (perhaps a later addition), this is not a series of quick pen and ink sketches, but in some cases is preceded by a preparatory pencil drawing that was later gone over in ink in the final version. These preparatory drawings are proof that Leonardo aimed at a well-finished representation. Apart from the drawings inserted in the upper part of the page (some of the sketches are not completed and some were added perhaps at another time), the entirety of notes and images on this folio is complete unto itself. There is the main image of the entire wing, right and left, and some enlarged details. Even the two main blocks of text are singularly regular. All this recalls the typical character of the mechanical studies Leonardo inserts in the Madrid I manuscript, and in general, it recalls the type of studies undertaken during the 1490s in all aspects of his research. This is a period of great intellectual equilibrium, dominated by a geometrical and mathematical concept of natural phenomena, reflected not only by the content of his research but also by the clear graphic organisation of the page, the regularity in line and hatching – very close and fine – an example of which is seen in the main drawing on this folio.

His studies on flight during these years are a result of his research on the dynamic potentiality of the human body. The study and imitation of birds seems now to fall into second place. Some of his studies and projects are an exception to this, and among these are the contents of this page: the wing is made up of various segments jointed together and moved by cables. Leonardo has provided us with an imitation of the anatomical joints of the natural wing.

In this case, the various parts are at right angles to each other. Later when he is working on the Codex 'On the Flight of Birds' and the observation and imitation of natural flight are once again in the forefront, the structural segments even take on the shape of animal bones, pushing the idea of human flight as an imitation of nature to its utmost.

fig. 1
Folio 844r in the Codex Atlanticus, with its well-defined drawings, shows the centre part of a project for a mechanical wing that seems to imitate the anatomy and workings of animal wings.

fig. 2
The image shows the reconstruction of the detail found in the upper right of the folio in fig. 1.

overleaf, following page
fig. 3
This image shows the digital reconstruction of the project on folio 844r from the Codex Atlanticus in its entirety and placed on top of the drawing itself.

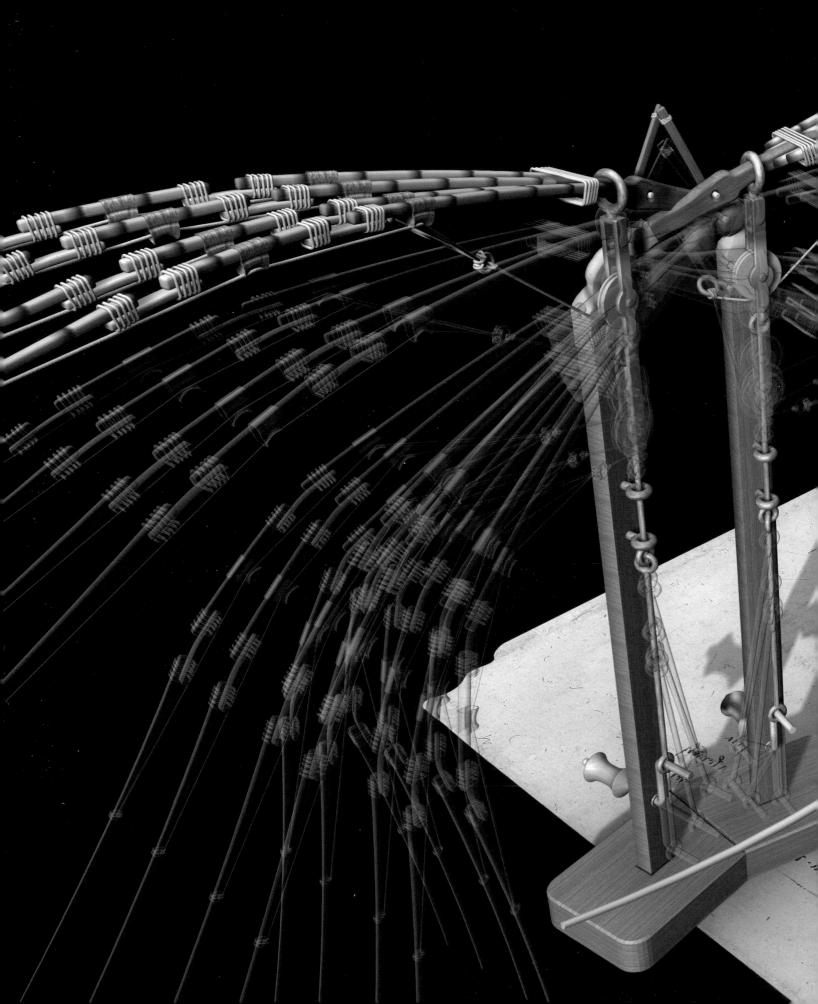

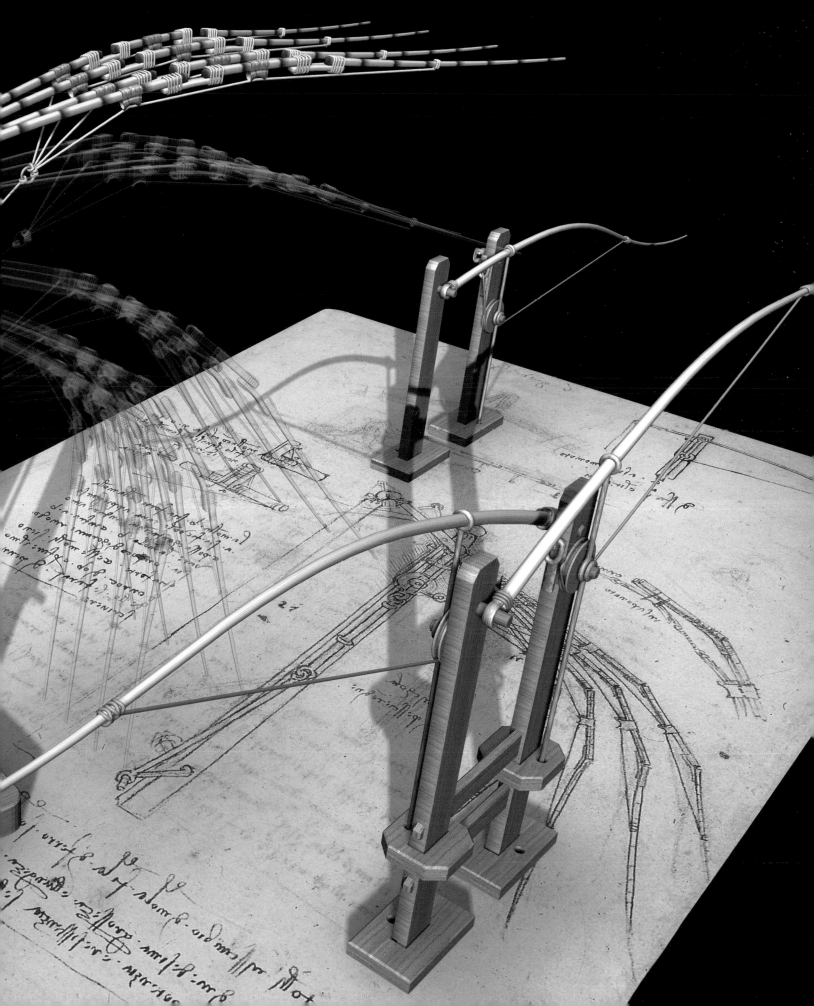

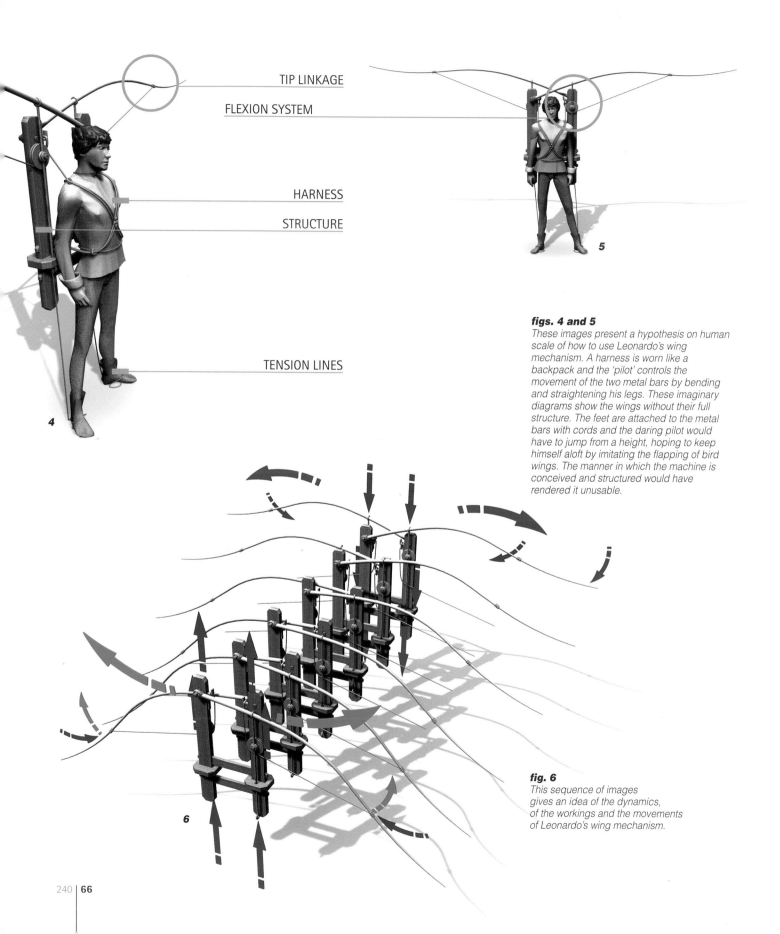

TIP LINKAGE

FLEXION SYSTEM

HARNESS

STRUCTURE

TENSION LINES

4

5

figs. 4 and 5
These images present a hypothesis on human scale of how to use Leonardo's wing mechanism. A harness is worn like a backpack and the 'pilot' controls the movement of the two metal bars by bending and straightening his legs. These imaginary diagrams show the wings without their full structure. The feet are attached to the metal bars with cords and the daring pilot would have to jump from a height, hoping to keep himself aloft by imitating the flapping of bird wings. The manner in which the machine is conceived and structured would have rendered it unusable.

6

fig. 6
This sequence of images gives an idea of the dynamics, of the workings and the movements of Leonardo's wing mechanism.

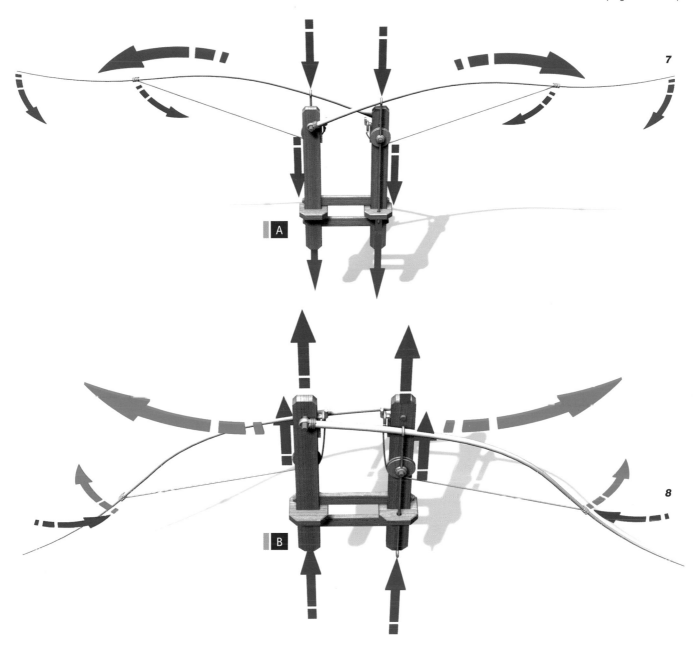

figs. 7 and 8
*The images schematically show
the operating principle of the mechanical arm
in the two phases of folding-flexion
and spreading-extension of the wings.*

A This first image outlines the dynamics behind the operation of the wing in the flexion phase. The two metals arms are pulled down (blue arrows) along the parallel support stays, the wing slides through the end rings on the arms. This movement results in a downward rotation of the wing itself. The pulley system used to move the metal arms pulls a line connected to the wing tip. As they rotate, the pulleys wind the line that folds in the end of the wing (red arrows).

B In the second phase, the wing is re-opened and extended using the same flexion principle in reverse. The metal arms move upward; the wings slide through the end rings on the arms, they re-open and the pulleys let out the line so that the wing, from a folded position, can now be extended.

fig. 9
*The image shows the disassembled model
of the wing machine with all its parts.*

9

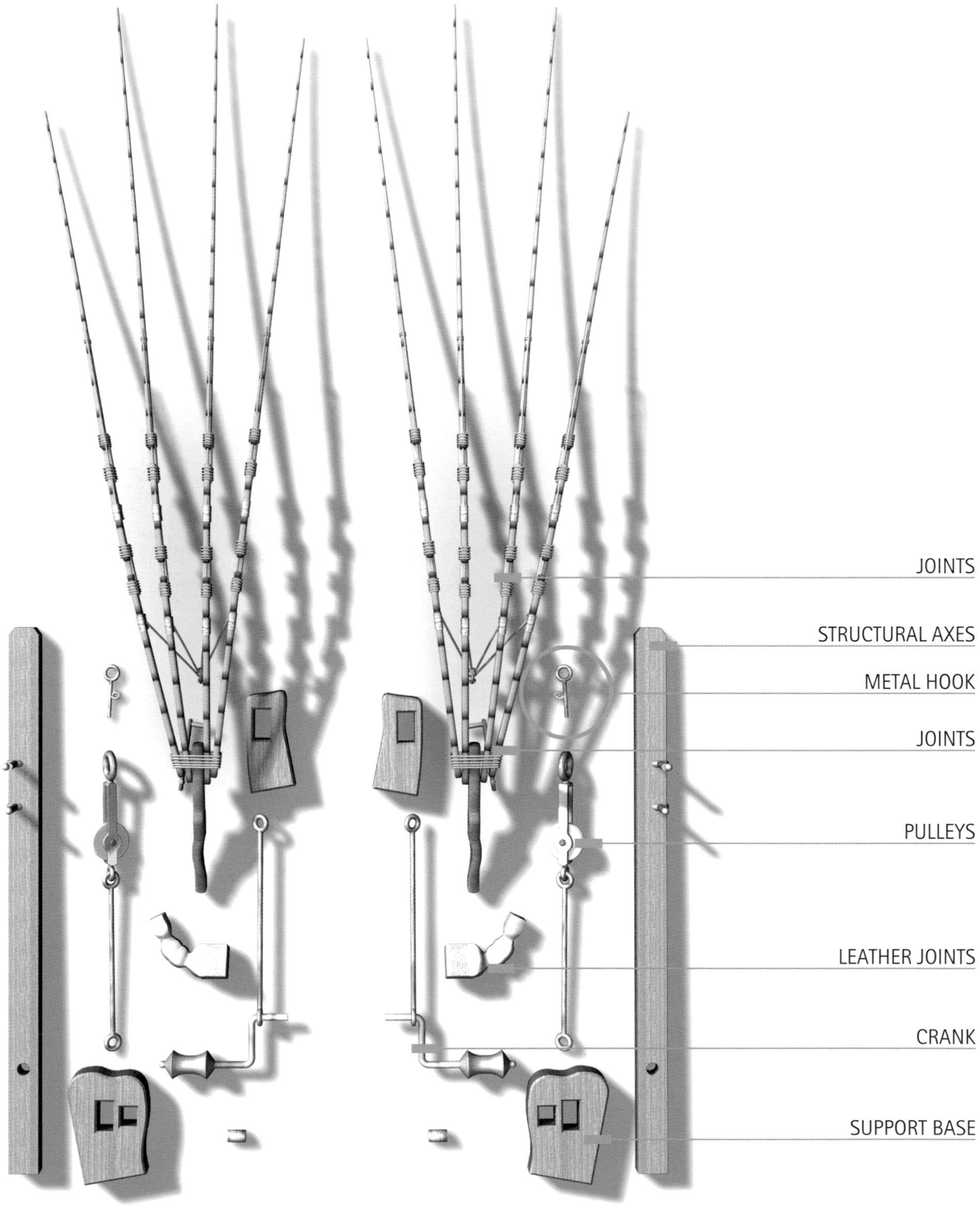

JOINTS

STRUCTURAL AXES

METAL HOOK

JOINTS

PULLEYS

LEATHER JOINTS

CRANK

SUPPORT BASE

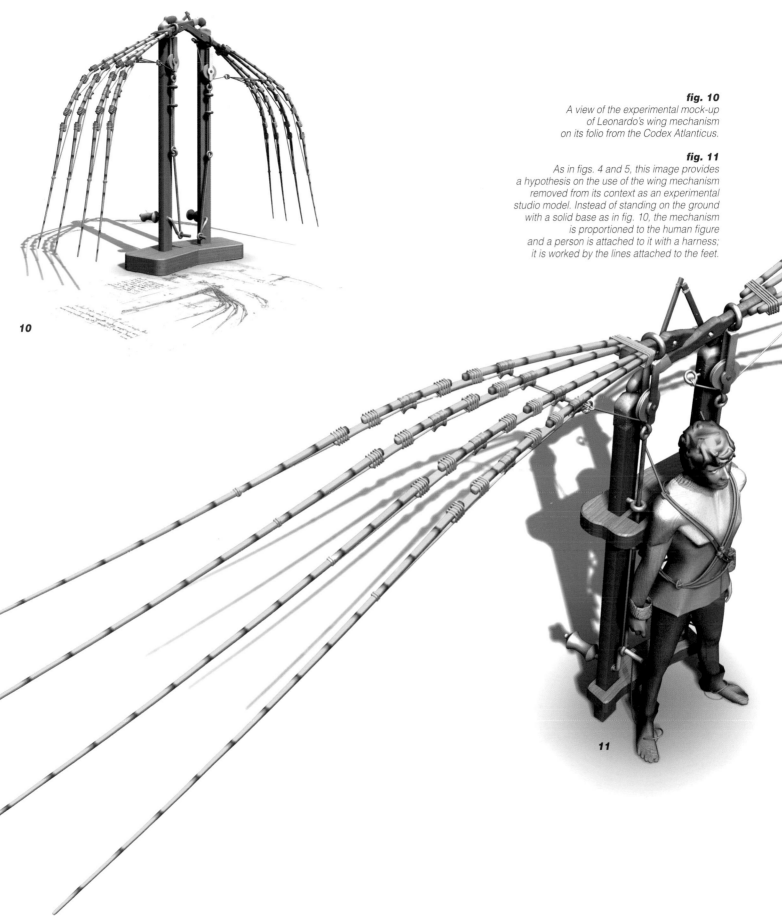

fig. 10
*A view of the experimental mock-up
of Leonardo's wing mechanism
on its folio from the Codex Atlanticus.*

fig. 11
*As in figs. 4 and 5, this image provides
a hypothesis on the use of the wing mechanism
removed from its context as an experimental
studio model. Instead of standing on the ground
with a solid base as in fig. 10, the mechanism
is proportioned to the human figure
and a person is attached to it with a harness;
it is worked by the lines attached to the feet.*

10

11

For the most part, Leonardo designs and works on war machines during his first few years in Milan (between about 1483-1490), and upon his return to Florence around 1502-1504. The projects designed in Milan are more varied, more spectacular than later works but often at the very limits of feasibility. Leonardo's subsequent projects in this field are more rigorous, and they concentrate on both the main defensive and offensive concerns of military strategy of the time: firearms. A large portion of the introduction letter Leonardo writes to Ludovico il Moro (Codex Atlanticus, f. 1082r) deals with military engineering: bridges, assault ladders, bombards, carriages, mortars. Leonardo is about thirty years old when he decides to make a change in his career and when he composes this letter, requesting assistance from a man of letters who puts it in 'bella forma'. He has already left, or is about to leave Florence, offering his services to the warrior-price Ludovico Sforza. It would not be far-fetched to hypothesise that the letter may have been accompanied by some illustrative drawings. The Codex Atlanticus (a collection of originally loose sheets, improperly defined as 'codex') contains some magnificent drawings of war machines; very well-finished drawings that could have been part of a sumptuous album to be presented to il Moro. This may help to explain some of these projects and their spectacular, extra-ordinary character: gigantic machines with terrifying effects often difficult or impossible to actually produce. If, as is almost certain, Leonardo's letter was written during the period he transferred from Florence to Milan, it is also quite clear that in his earlier years in Florence he must have dedicated time to studying machines used for war. In the past, other Tuscan engineers such as Taccola or Francesco di Giorgio had also dealt with this subject. Young Leonardo is aware of the tradition that precedes him, and this tradition certainly influenced his initial projects designed between Florence and the early part of his Milanese sojourn. For example, his drawings for obsidional machines (meant to assail fortress walls) reflecting to a certain degree the studies of other engineers, are part of the same sensitivity and interest towards antiquity that was typical of the Renaissance. In addition to being an actual art practised on the battlefield, war is also a cultural fact, one aspect of the general rediscovery of the classical world. One of the most successful military treatises to come out of the Renaissance, *De re militari*, written around 1450-1455 by Roberto Valturio, is a reconstruction of the main war machines used by the ancients; and Valturio is a humanist, not an engineer. In Urbino, war machines are the subjects of architectural decoration, as demonstrated by the bas-relief frieze with war machines in the Palazzo Ducale. Obsidional machines were among the most typical manifestations of the art of war during classical times and in designing some of these, Leonardo participates in the rediscovery of classicism. Even his confidence in the value of drawing as a means of communication connects Leonardo with Taccola or Francesco di Giorgio. Leonardo, however, transcends tradition not only because of the superior quality of his drawings or the varied and innovative visual formulas used in presenting the project (images from various viewpoints, full and exploded views, etc.), but also in the complexity of conceptual content expressed through the visual language of the machine. If we compare the drawings of machines that Francesco di Giorgio inserted in his treatises with drawings made for artistic purposes, the difference between these two types of drawing is evident. Like those by Leonardo, the mechanical drawings by Francesco also demonstrate, through theoretical declarations, his absolute confidence in drawing as a means of communicating knowledge. From the viewpoint of description and perspective his drawings are very precise. Nevertheless, because they are an integral part of the treatise text they have a didactic, scholastic character. This 'gap' between mechanical drawing and artistic drawing is completely surpassed by Leonardo, as is evident in his drawing depicting a device for pushing away the ladders of assault troops scaling a fortress wall (Codex Atlanticus, f. 139r) or, even more evident, in the drawing of an enormous cannon in a foundry (Windsor 12647) where, in addition to the mechanical concept, Leonardo depicts the movement of the human figures. The nudity of many of the labourers in the foundry can be explained only by the displacement of technological drawing towards a more general, expressive dimension that in this case is intent on demonstrating the forcefulness of the bodies while working. Later, this theme will intrigue Leonardo not only as a painter but also in relation to his work on human flight. Even when he draws the terrible scythed chariots (on a folio found in the Biblioteca Reale at Turin, and another in the British Museum, London), the mechanical representation is transformed into a dramatic image emphasising the horrible wounds the weapon would have been able to inflict. Images of human bodies torn to pieces, slashed and ripped to shreds, are accompanied by his annotation on these devices: 'often they wreak as much havoc on friends as on foes'. About 1504 in Florence, this dual dimension is again seen in an even more striking form: on a folio from the Codex Atlanticus (72v) the study for a firearm is next to the drawing of a horse for the *Battle of Anghiari*, the large painting commissioned by the Florentine Republic for a room in the Palazzo Vecchio.

Some of the machines designed by Leonardo in the early part of his career are more practical, simpler and can be constructed on the spot: the projects for emergency bridges, swing bridges (Codex Atlanticus 55r, 855r) for quickly crossing bodies of water, the various forms of ladders for assailing a fortress (for example, Manuscript B, ff. 50r and 59v), and the numerous and unusual lance points (for example, Codex Ashburnham 2037).

Here again, drawing seems to go beyond just a practical application, and lances and ladders seem to transform themselves into anthologies of images inspired by an unrestrainable formal inventiveness. In 1499, when the French drive the Sforza out of Milan, the entire political situation of the peninsula turns increasingly unstable. His contacts and the work that Leonardo takes on in the years immediately prior to his eventual abandonment of Milan are an indicator of this reality. Perhaps he comes into contact with the French while he is in Milan, contacts made in preparation for a military operation to be undertaken in the southern part of the peninsula. Once leaving Milan, Leonardo is consulted by the Venetian Republic on the problem of the military defence of its eastern territories and the danger posed by the Ottoman Empire. In 1502, Leonardo is working for Cesare Borgia, il Valentino, in the territorial conquest of the Romagna region. Once again for military reasons, he is contacted by Jacopo IV Appiani the Lord of Piombino, and by the Florentine Republic engaged in on-going war against Pisa. In this backdrop, Leonardo initiates his new studies in military engineering, studies that are quite different compared to those of the Sforza years. Now Leonardo is faced with concrete problems relating to war, and now, more than in the previous period the proposed solutions are more rigorous, more thought-out and truly innovative. Having put aside the gigantic crossbows and spectacular but improbable catapults, Leonardo concentrates on facing the great innovation of the century: the ever-increasing use of firearms with their destructive capabilities already defined by Francesco di Giorgio as a 'diabolic invention'. During the first few years of the 1500s Leonardo constantly confronts this innovation, and he analyses both the defensive and offensive aspects. Some incredible projects for fortresses come from this period (for example, Codex Atlanticus 120v, 132r, 133r), where the shape of the edifice is designed to minimise the impact from artillery. Fortresses constructed without straight, vertical walls, but with a curved profile to absorb the shock of the blows and deflect them away. There are also studies on artillery. The invention of a rotating armament made up of sixteen guns mounted on the same platform (Codex Atlanticus, f. 1r) may date from this period. The fundamental goal of this project is to provide as much firepower as possible, the same goal demonstrated in a few of his beautiful ballistic studies on defence systems for a stronghold (Windsor 12337v, 12275r, Codex Atlanticus f. 72v). It is stunning to observe Leonardo's skill in depicting the shower of shot and shells, accurately describing their parabolic trajectories. The tight, interwoven lines rendering the trajectories of the shots 'visible' are drawn by Leonardo with the sureness of one who has dedicated much time and attention to the subject.

Vinci, 1452

1460

1470

1480

circa 1482

1490

1500

1510

Amboise, 1519

Codex Atlanticus, f. 32r

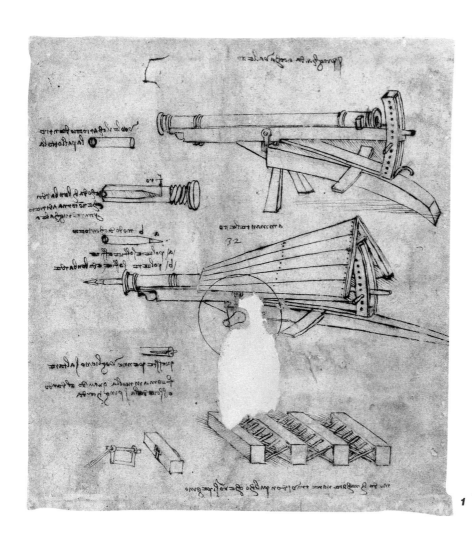

1

Springald

2

The calligraphy in the written notes on this sheet is typical of Leonardo's earlier period, characterised by an elegant style with frequent flourishes and other graphic ornamentation. Nevertheless, it is the image that is important in these drawings: the written notes provide a few clarifications about details, but the description of the project for the springald is essentially left to visual language. Prior to Leonardo, some of the great artist-engineers of the *Quattrocento* had already begun to make claim to the intellectual nature of drawing, and thereby to the scientific value in the invention and construction of machines. This process reached its zenith with Leonardo, as seen in this drawing from his early years. During the Middle Ages at times machines were the subject of illustrations, depicted in their exterior aspect according to a series of iconographical conventions. At times the unusual character of these images created amazement and marvel, conferring an almost miraculous sense to the machines. But completely missing from the formula was information on the structure, the internal form, the relationship between the parts, the workings. There was little or nothing revealed about the machine itself, perhaps because it was considered to be a professional secret, or perhaps what was truly important was the miraculous aspect of the device, independent from its realisation. Instead, the drawings inserted by Leonardo on this sheet are meant to communicate by using the two main drawings as compliments to one another and through the details isolated from the full drawing, the number, the form, the functioning and most importantly, the reciprocal relationship between the various structural elements of the machine. The two main images show two views of the springald: above, the structural nucleus of the weapon (the cannon and its elevating arc, the tripod support, etc.); below, it has a protective roof with the wheels used for moving the weapon barely hinted at. Here some very important iconographical concepts are being used. In the lower figure, Leonardo delineates a simple circle around the axle to represent the wheel: a transparent image that is enough to express the way the mechanism moves. He leaves the structure behind the wheel in view, and thereby, the relationship between wheel and springald. Later on, Leonardo will draw anatomical figures in transparency, attempting to demonstrate the reciprocal relationship between the various organs of the body. In fact, many iconographical solutions initially devised for depicting machines are carried over into other areas of research. Even the relationship between the two main images on this page anticipates some of visual presentations later applied to anatomy: the full image of the springald (below) is stripped (above) of its exterior components (cover and wheels), just as occurs in the process of anatomical dissection.

fig. 1
An extremely clear drawing not requiring much explanation; just as Leonardo sustained, a picture is worth a thousand words.

fig. 2
The cannon has just been cast and is waiting to be mounted on the springald.

overleaf, following page, fig. 3
An overhead view of the springald; the lines and wedges helped anchor the tripod structure due to the powerful shot and recoil, and to facilitate the manoeuvres for aiming the cannon.

fig. 4
An exploded view of all the parts of the springald before being mounted.

A The largest and most important element of the machine is certainly the massive cannon. It was placed on a very strong and moveable wooden structure so as to effectively aim the weapon. The innovative aspect of Leonardo's springald was precisely its mobility and the possibility of aiming in different directions without moving the entire cannon or tripod. In fact, presumably whoever used this firearm positioned himself on the battlefield and anchored it to the ground. Due to the fact that the recoil from the large cannon must have been very powerful, the frame could be anchored in place by lines attached to wedges planted in the ground. Tied down in this fashion the support structure was very stabile; the cannon, however, could move freely from right to left, as well as up and down.

B Leonardo not only thinks about solutions to improve and speed-up the aiming phase, but he also comes up with a system of fast-loading ammunition without intervening on the internal parts of the cannon. On the folio, he uses more than one drawing to show this ingenious system; more than one person could manoeuvre around the springald. There was the person in charge of positioning and aiming (one or more given the weight of the structure), but there also was a person who prepared and loaded the ammunition into the cannon.

C The aiming of the springald was done with two slides, one vertical and one horizontal. The cannon could be moved and adjusted on these two planes, thereby covering an extensive firing range. The cannon had great freedom of movement, but it could not cover all the directions on the battlefront; we can imagine that in a hypothetical battle scene more than one springald may have been used, all aimed onto the main targets. The complex orientation system for the cannon that Leonardo studied probably was used more for taking precise aim than for choosing one target rather than another.

3

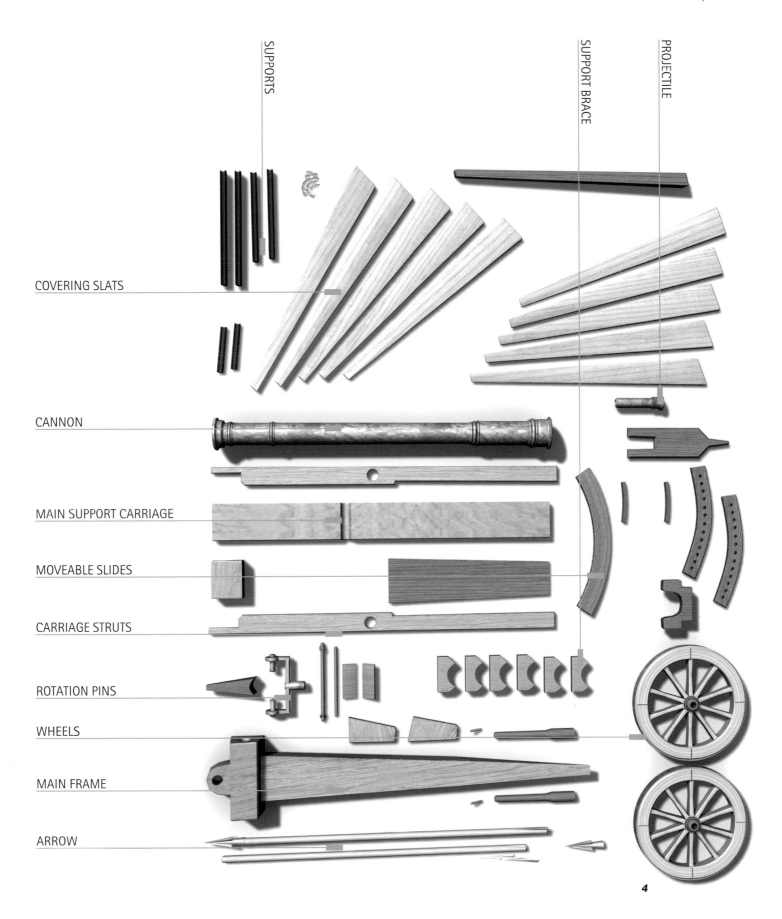

SUPPORTS

SUPPORT BRACE

PROJECTILE

COVERING SLATS

CANNON

MAIN SUPPORT CARRIAGE

MOVEABLE SLIDES

CARRIAGE STRUTS

ROTATION PINS

WHEELS

MAIN FRAME

ARROW

4

A The cannon could be moved both on a vertical as well as horizontal plane. The cannon was positioned horizontally by dragging the mount supporting the cannon housing along a curved wooden piece. Lubricated to slide more easily, the curved shape of this piece was also used as a guide in obtaining an even, quick rotation without jerking. The amplitude of its action could cover an arc of about 20 to 30 degrees.

B The vertical movement of the cannon was slightly more complex and the adjustments in this direction were less manageable. In order to regulate the firing elevation the entire cannon and its structure had to be raised; the tripod was the only piece of the springald anchored to the ground. The moveable carriage was pinned to the structure with by a mechanical joint, and thus the movement of the cannon was surely much easier, but in order to raise it even a few degrees certainly more than one person was needed. Once the desired elevation was attained, a peg consisting in a simple cylinder made of wood or iron was inserted in the appropriate holes thus blocking the structure. This adjustment calibrated the range of fire, and was probably the first operation undertaken. Once the correct elevation adjustments were complete, the cannon could be turned from left to right much more easily.

C Leonardo designs some very interesting projectiles: they consisted of a detonation chamber filled with two different types of gunpowder and the shot. When ready, the cartridge was loaded, and could be quickly substituted with another round already prepared, avoiding reloading the cannon from the muzzle each time. The operators could prepare many rounds and breechload them very quickly from the rear of the cannon.

fig. 5
Diagram of the workings: the structure and the cannon were probably so heavy that more than one person was needed to operate it.

fig. 6
Leonardo's project is not only interesting in terms of how the springald was used but also because he devised different variations on the same machine: a fixed tripod with or without the wheels, closed under a covering, or in a open position. Also, this springald could fire iron or stone cannonballs as well as metal-tipped arrows. The image presents the composition on Leonardo's folio where we also see a strange wooden frame; with reference to this Leonardo writes: 'Way to fit beams in a scaffolding so they won't bend'.

C

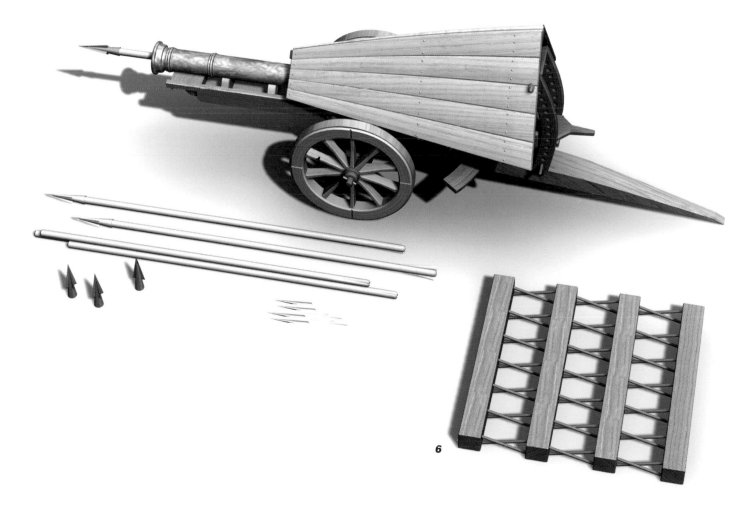

6

Vinci, 1452

1460
1470
1480
circa 1482
1490
1500
1510

Amboise, 1519

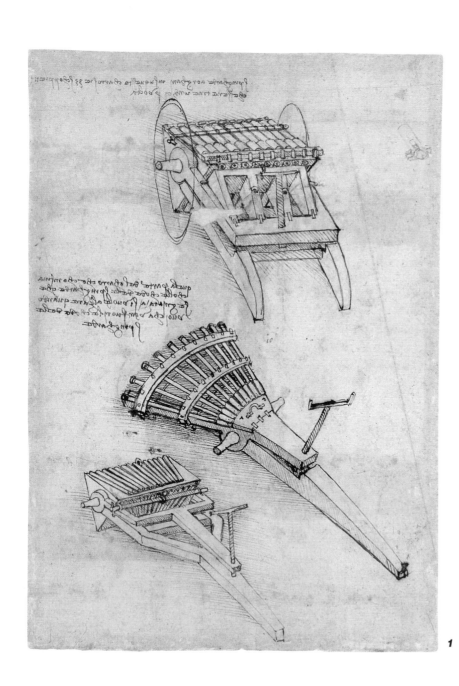

1

Multi-barrelled Machine Gun

2

The page shows three alternative projects for a machine gun. In presenting them, Leonardo does not follow the same spatial perspective. Not only is there a size difference between the three drawings, but they also seem different from an optical viewpoint. This creates a less orderly and systematic layout on the page, but adds movement to the presentation by emphasising the variety in the projects and avoiding a monotonous sequence of alternating objects found in drawings by other engineers and even on some pages by Leonardo. Above, a simple circle suggests the position and size of the wheel, with the parts for the wheel connection in transparency. Below, only the axle is drawn suggesting the position of the wheel, while greater attention is given to the screw system regulating the height (in the upper project this seems fairly flat). The three images complete and compliment one another following a perfect system of visual shorthand that does not infringe upon the specifics and individuality of the single project.

Innovative design in firearms, weapons that were in the vanguard at the time, was an excellent way of creating interest and amazement in a prospective client. But for whom is Leonardo designing these lethal instruments? Based on the style of both the drawing and the writing, scholars date this folio to his period in Florence. At that time, around 1480, the political situation in the peninsula has not yet exploded. The dominant figure in Florence is Lorenzo the Magnificent, and thanks to a tightly woven web of diplomatic relationships he is also one of the mainstays of the temporary and relatively peaceful period. Nonetheless, as the bloody Pazzi conspiracy against the Medici demonstrates, tensions and hostilities are spreading. Thus, even in Florence war is always an immediate possibility. The greatest Florentine engineers and architects dealt with war, from Brunelleschi to Michelozzo, and even Verrocchio's workshop where Leonardo apprenticed was capable of casting cannons and armour. Consequently, young Leonardo's interest in warfare is totally understandable. But there is another, perhaps even more convincing explanation. Just as for other Tuscan colleagues Leonardo can not wait to leave his homeland and go into the service of a powerful warrior-prince. Taccola had already dreamed of going into service of the emperor of Hungary, and Francesco di Giorgio was very successful working in Urbino under Federico da Montefeltro. We do not know if Leonardo had already decided to go to Milan when he made this 'bella copia' of military drawings. What is certain is that when he does decide to go his main calling card will be his wartime projects.

fig. 1
The sheet contains three separate projects for a machine gun, along with some handwritten notes.

fig. 2
A machine gun completed and ready for firing; project on the centre on the page.

overleaf, following page, figs. 3 and 4
Two projects on the page. The strong point in both solutions is the strength of their firepower, but with totally different working principles.

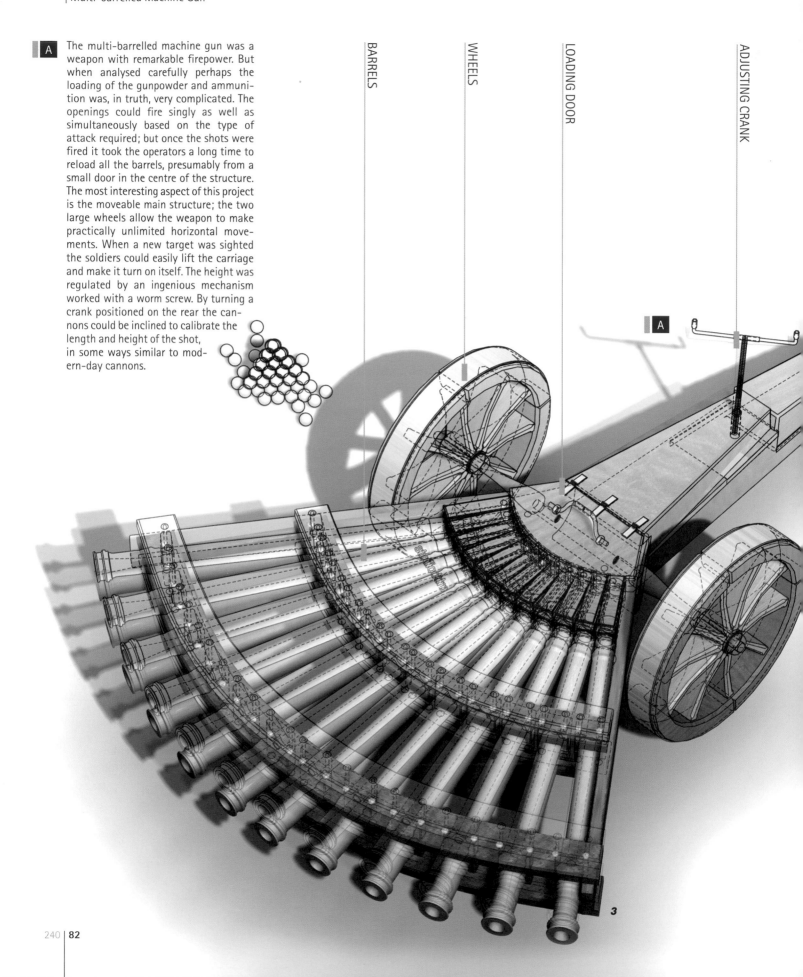

A The multi-barrelled machine gun was a weapon with remarkable firepower. But when analysed carefully perhaps the loading of the gunpowder and ammunition was, in truth, very complicated. The openings could fire singly as well as simultaneously based on the type of attack required; but once the shots were fired it took the operators a long time to reload all the barrels, presumably from a small door in the centre of the structure. The most interesting aspect of this project is the moveable main structure; the two large wheels allow the weapon to make practically unlimited horizontal movements. When a new target was sighted the soldiers could easily lift the carriage and make it turn on itself. The height was regulated by an ingenious mechanism worked with a worm screw. By turning a crank positioned on the rear the cannons could be inclined to calibrate the length and height of the shot, in some ways similar to modern-day cannons.

BARRELS

WHEELS

LOADING DOOR

ADJUSTING CRANK

A

3

B A second design on the upper portion of the page illustrates a different machine gun. In this case all the cannons fire in the same direction and they do not have as wide a range of action as in the previous project; the interesting aspect of this machine is the possibility of rotating the large triangular central body. On each side of this structure there are many cannons, all pre-loaded and ready to fire on the target. A rear bulkhead acts as support and block for the central body; in fact, when it is fired it turns around influencing the direction of the shot. Like the previous machine, this weapon required long reloading times.

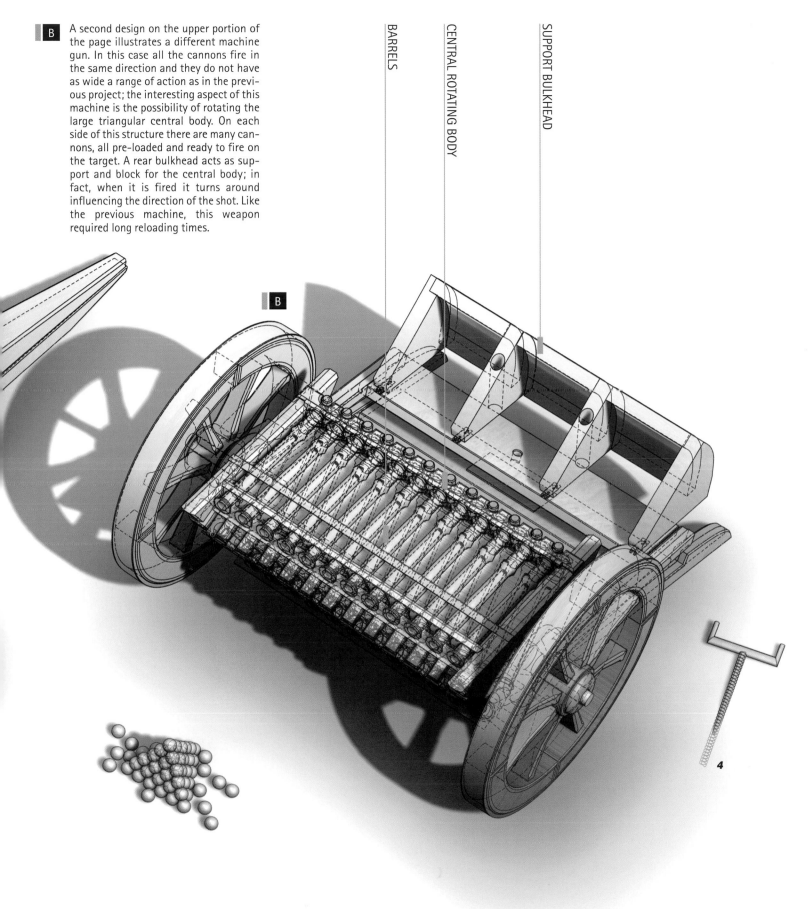

BARRELS

CENTRAL ROTATING BODY

SUPPORT BULKHEAD

B

4

Vinci, 1452

1460

1470

1480

1482-1485

1490

1500

1510

Amboise, 1519

Codex Atlanticus, f. 139r

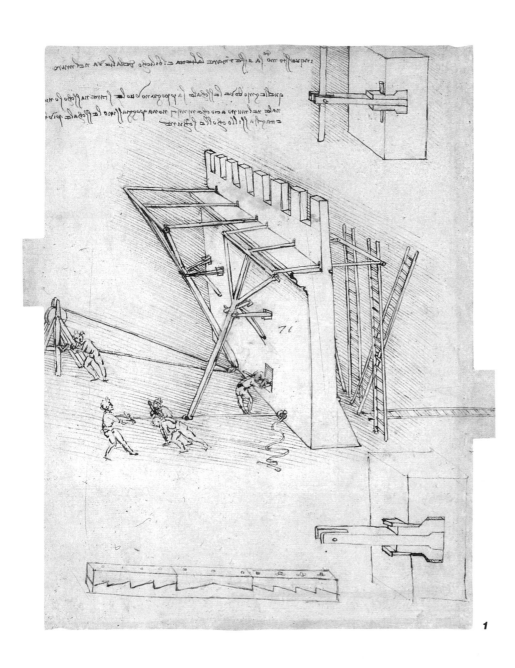

1

Defence of the Walls

2

Dating from Leonardo's early years of activity, the drawing belongs to a very special category of his oldest designs: the transformation of the mechanical drawing into complex action, depicted by a small-scale drama with human protagonists and spatial references. One of the greatest Sienese engineers of the *Quattrocento*, Mariano di Jacopo, called 'il Taccola', created small vignettes with machines placed in different types of landscapes. But in Leonardo this contextual presentation is much more complex, and in a certain sense, is on the opposite end of the other iconographical innovation he developed: machines depicted in isolation from every environmental element. This drawing studies a defence system for battlements consisting of a beam hidden in the walls that can push off assault ladders, and here, both iconographical concepts are present. In fact, Leonardo creates an image exemplary in its synthesis, an image that gives maximum information in minimum space, while the men working the device create a highly dramatic and effective scene. Leonardo shows only part of the wall: it is an image that is not realistic, a technical and theoretical representation. In the same drawing, he also presents a dual possibility for operating the system: direct traction using more than one person, or, a mechanical system requiring only one person. Even the system of levers and beams is shown in advancing and retracting positions. Some of the enlarged details, above and below, complete the most self-sufficient part of this mechanical image; but that has still another aspect. The dynamic efforts of the small figures working the device are shown in agitated movement highlighted by the hatching. As in analogous cases, the vibrant hatched lines not only provide spatial indications, but seem to be the echo or outburst of the dynamism of the figures. Animated in this way the image is transformed into much more than a simple mechanical drawing. The minute but very effective style that with a few lines defines the form and movement of the various human figures, is the same we find in artistic drawings such as the studies made in this period for the *Adoration of the Magi*. In reality, the distinction that we make today between artistic and scientific or technical drawing is much more ephemeral for Leonardo and his time. A technological drawing by Leonardo can always be enjoyed as a sublime artistic image.

fig. 1
The folio shows the moment of assault on the walls of a castle, while the people on the inside activate the mechanism devised by Leonardo.

fig. 2
The winch use to activate the system for the defence of the battlements.

A The assault on castles and fortresses using a rung ladder was a very frequent strategy during the 1500s; the assailants placed the ladders against the walls until they overran the battlements fighting against the defenders in great numbers. Once the walls were scaled and after heavy losses, the assault of the castle went on and the assailants, now inside, could destroy the gates letting in their fellow warriors. For the defenders it was therefore of vital importance to prevent the assailants from scaling the walls.

B Leonardo designs an ingenious system of defence to prevent enemies from scaling the walls. A long beam, on the exterior of the walls, was pushed against the ladders by a series of winches attached to a system that functioned like a lever. When the beam pushed the ladders, having a capacity to push even more than one at the same time, they fell to the ground along with the assailants.

C The external beam was attached to the internal winch by a series of perpendicular beams that went through the holes in the wall. On the ground below, the lever transformed the traction of one or more persons working the winch into a sudden, powerful push externally. Once the push was made, and the desired results obtained, the beam was retracted taking it out of the range of any harm that could be inflicted by the enemy; in this way the device could have been used an unlimited number of times.

D The most ingenious aspect of this project is the way the supports are fitted to the lever. Leonardo resorted to a particular use of geometry: he needed the support beams to be fit into the walls in a secure system that could not be attacked from the exterior, and when needed, could be dismantled or repaired.

fig. 3
Detail of the system used for fitting the beams in the wall.

fig. 4
How the system worked.

figs. 5 and 6
Two views of the walls with their main parts; the first view is from inside the castle, the second is from the exterior, from the points of view, respectively, of the defenders and the assailants.

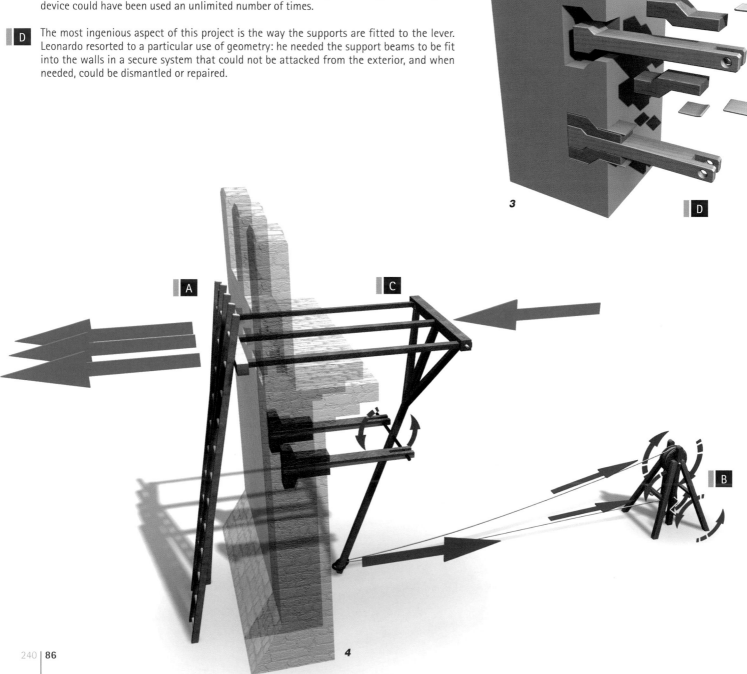

3   **D**

A   **C**

B

4

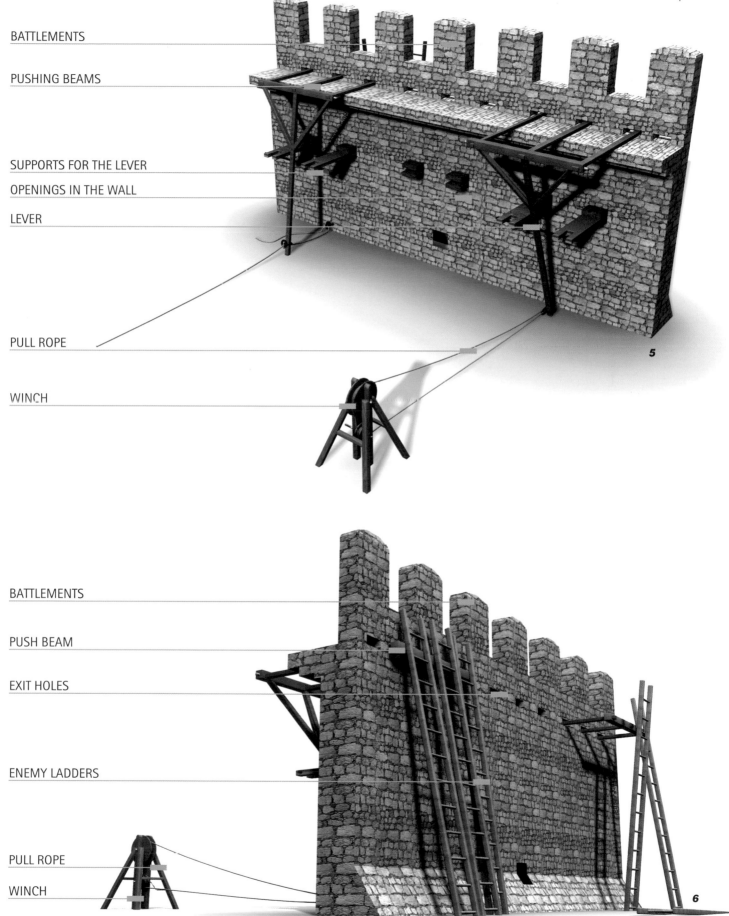

BATTLEMENTS

PUSHING BEAMS

SUPPORTS FOR THE LEVER

OPENINGS IN THE WALL

LEVER

PULL ROPE

WINCH

5

BATTLEMENTS

PUSH BEAM

EXIT HOLES

ENEMY LADDERS

PULL ROPE

WINCH

6

Vinci, 1452

1460

1470

1480

circa 1485

1490

1500

1510

Amboise, 1519

Turin, Bibl. Reale, f. 15583r

1

Scythed Chariots

2

Among Leonardo's most spectacular drawings for machines dating from the first few years in Milan there are two studies for carriages armed with scythes. War was the order of the day on the unstable political chessboard of Renaissance Italy and Europe. War machines were often at the centre of interest during this period, not only for their practical use but also for purely cultural reasons; for example, the rediscovery of inventions from classical times. They were unusual and visually striking, independent of the fact that the machines could be actually constructed. The famous frieze in the ducal palace at Urbino with sculpted panels depicting a series of war machines, the sumptuous albums consisting solely in images of machines and the minimal text are created in this context. The image has the same value as reality, and more than in any other age, we who live in a virtual era should know how to appreciate this aspect of the Renaissance. Leonardo's two drawings on this folio conserved in Turin fit perfectly into this dimension dominated by the machine as a visual invention. Even though Leonardo provides us with some information on the mechanical workings of the two war chariots, we have in front of us two images where the intent is to give a general idea of the weapon's lethal power as a whole. As in other drawings from this period, the mechanical drawing is transformed into a dramatic spectacle dominated by the furious movements of the human figures and animals that operate or fall victim to the machines. In this case there is even a sense of uneasiness about the machine as a cause of death, a sentiment expressed by Leonardo in a note where he specifies that these contraptions 'often wreak as much havoc on friends as on foes'. Many years later, Leonardo will define war as 'beastly madness', creating a metaphoric image of this condemnation in the *Battle of Anghiari*, where the furious combatants take on beastly, animallike movements and expressions. This vision is at the basis of Leonardo's mature work, and is already embryonically present in these two mechanical figures, especially in the upper drawing where the lethal scythes have slaughtered a group of armoured soldiers. Perhaps drawings such as these accompanied the letter Leonardo presented to Ludovico il Moro upon his arrival in Milan. It would have been difficult for the powerful and bellicose Lord of Milan to grasp the subtle reflections in these drawings, and consequently this is perhaps the reason why Leonardo's proposals for war machinery were not given consideration at court. Other engineers, less ingenious but more practical were preferred; at least for awhile.

fig. 1
A very explicit depiction of two different models of scythed chariots in battle.

fig. 2
A spiked-wheel as drawn on Leonardo's folio.

A In Leonardo's drawing there is a team of horses positioned at the centre of this scythed chariot. Putting aside the problems of space and peril, the hypothesis must be that once in battle, horses pulled the entire system.

B A team of horses pulled the chariot and traction was obtained by two large, spiked-wheels. One of the wheels had rungs and it transmitted rotary motion to the main cage-shaped gear. There were also two rotating blades mounted on the wheels to prevent the enemy from approaching.

C The main cage-shaped gear, turned by the wheels, transmits rotary energy to the two blade systems, front and rear.

D The rotating dual blades prevent the enemy from approaching the carriage from the rear.

E By means of a long drive shaft, the rotary motion is transmitted to the front gear system that works the main weapon on the carriage, a structure composed of four scythe blades.

fig. 3
Detail of the structure with four rotating scythe blades positioned on the front of the chariot.

fig. 4
Exploded view of the scythed chariot.

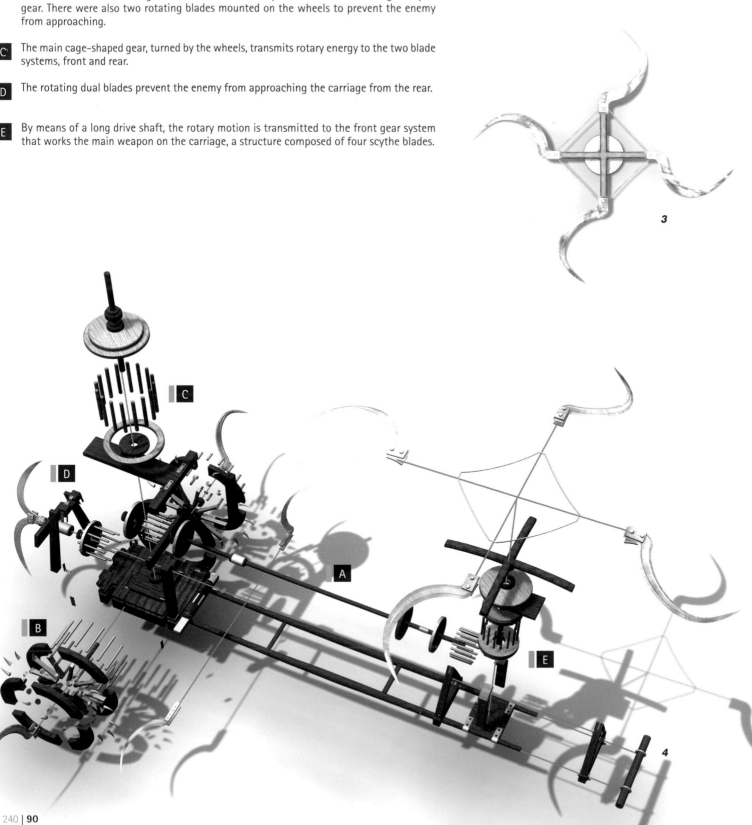

3

4

fig. 5

Like many of Leonardo's machines energy was transmitted by a gear train. In this case, two horses provide the propulsion power. A careful analysis of the gears demonstrates to the more observant readers that there could be operating errors in both the drawing and reconstruction. As in his armoured car project, it may be possible that Leonardo purposely inserted errors to conceal the correct functioning of the machine. Nevertheless, the appeal and charm of the page places any technical and structural inaccuracies in the background.

5

TRANSMISSION GEAR

MAIN CAGED-SHAPED GEAR

DRIVE SHAFT

SPIKED-WHEEL

METAL SPIKE

ROTATING BLADE

HITCH FOR HORSES

AUXILIARY BLADE

6

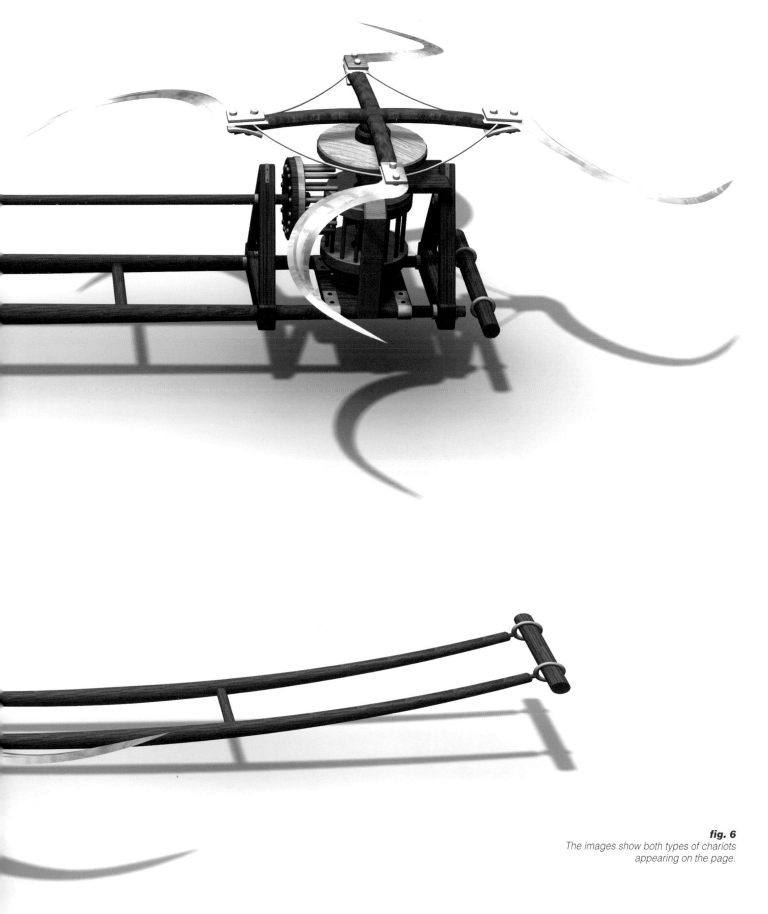

fig. 6
*The images show both types of chariots
appearing on the page.*

Vinci, 1452

1460

1470

1478-1485

1480

1490

1500

1510

Amboise, 1519

Codex Atlanticus, f. 154br

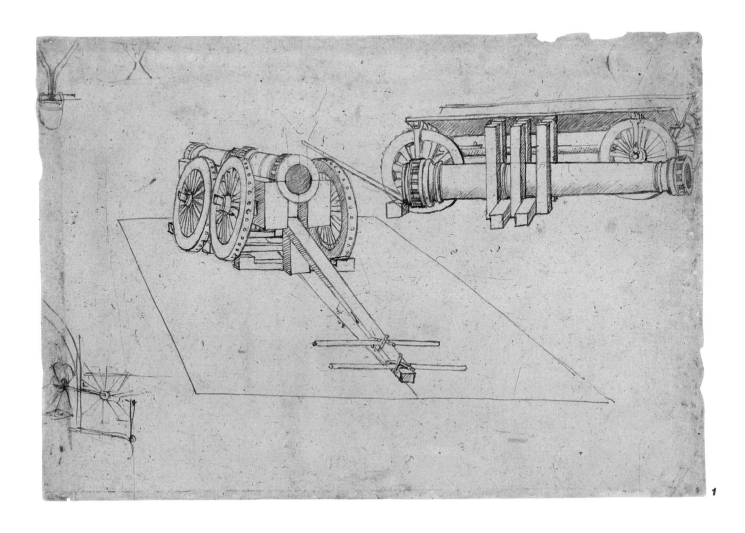

1

Dismountable Cannon

2

The history of the folio with the drawings for the dismountable cannon is exemplary of what happened to many of the Da Vincian pages. In fact, this is a fragment of a page that was originally larger in size, and along with other loose pages, was gathered together in the Codex Atlanticus (ff. 154, perhaps 73 and others). At the end of the sixteenth century, Pompeo Leone acquired a large number of Leonardo's sheets and manuscripts, binding them together in a collection of completely disordered pages known as the Codex Atlanticus. The predominantly mechanical subject of the papers was the only criteria he followed, and then only partially. Leone did not pose the problem of original order or whether the pages may have been part of an album or manuscript. He simply proceeded to take them apart in the name of a purely thematic criterion that may seem disrespectful to us today, but was well within the taste for erudite and encyclopaedic collections typical of the era. As demonstrated by the type of invention and its style, it is evident that Leonardo designed these two dismountable cannons during his early years. The drawing is not the best, and this fact might even tempt us to doubt Leonardo's authorship if it were not for the fact that the drawn line shows it was executed by a left-handed artist. It is a very well-finished drawing, not fruit of an immediate idea, but the good copy of studies made beforehand. Also, it can not be excluded that it is copied from another *maestro*, perhaps with an original variation inserted by Leonardo.

But, the story of this folio once the two drawings were finished has only just begun. Many years later after 1500, in the fragment of the original page, today gathered in the Codex Atlanticus and known as folio 154a, Leonardo once again takes up the idea of the cannon drawn on this page. The style of drawing and handwriting, and above all, the originality and maturity of these new projects are remarkably superior. Nonetheless, there is a link to the older drawing. This gives us a clear idea as to how Leonardo used an 'open entry system' in this work. Leafing through his papers after 1500, Leonardo's attention falls on the old project, which he now takes up again and develops. Or, it may be possible that in beginning a new project for a cannon, he returns to contemplate the older study, inserting new notes directly onto the old page. But that is not all. The page was circulated around the *maestro's* studio. Even though we can not exclude the possibility of an addition made in a later period, it is probable that one of the students inserted a quick sketch, obscene in character, very similar to those seen on other pages in the Codex Atlanticus. This type of quick 'sketch' is also found on other pages next to images with military studies (folios 132,133, 154b).

fig. 1
The page shows two distinct projects for dismountable cannons. The one in the centre is ready for use while the one drawn in the upper right still has to be mounted.

fig. 2
A cannon right after manufacture.

A The page contains two different projects for dismountable cannons. The structure for transporting a cannon can be very simple, but because it is a fairly uncomplicated project Leonardo attempts to solve some of the aspects brought about by the presence of a large cannon. The first of these is transporting the cannon over long distances and perhaps keeping it concealed in as compact and unobtrusive structure as possible. The main problem was the mounting of the structure, and in particular the moving of the cannon and its placement inside the structure. A few boards of wood appear in the drawing that could have been used for both protecting and lifting the cannon using a practical lever system. This type of solution would allow the heavy metal body to be housed on a cart and transported to the battle site without the use of other machines such as cranes or winches.

B The cannon in the centre drawing seems to be already mounted and ready to be transported or fired. There is a rod with four handles for hauling the carriage, leading us to believe that four people were necessary to move and manoeuvre the machine; the rod is interesting because on the part nearest to the frame there is a wedge. When the rod was lowered, the wedge probably lifted the carriage keeping it solidly anchored to the ground. Once the carriage was anchored and lifted slightly off the ground, sturdy stays were positioned to block the wheels while the shot was fired, most likely quite powerful given the size of the cannon. The wheel axles are inclined and the metal hoops have spikes on them: Leonardo understood that by inclining the axles the structure was much more solid. Most likely the wheels had spikes because on the battlefield the cannons had to be moved quickly over impervious and often slippery terrain.

ROD FOR HAULING

REAR STAYS

WHEELS WITH INCLINED AXLES

SPIKED-WHEEL HOOPS

3

B

fig. 3
The dismountable cannon ready for use with a description of the main parts.

fig. 4
A representation of the drawing on the upper part of the folio, where the cannon still has to be mounted.

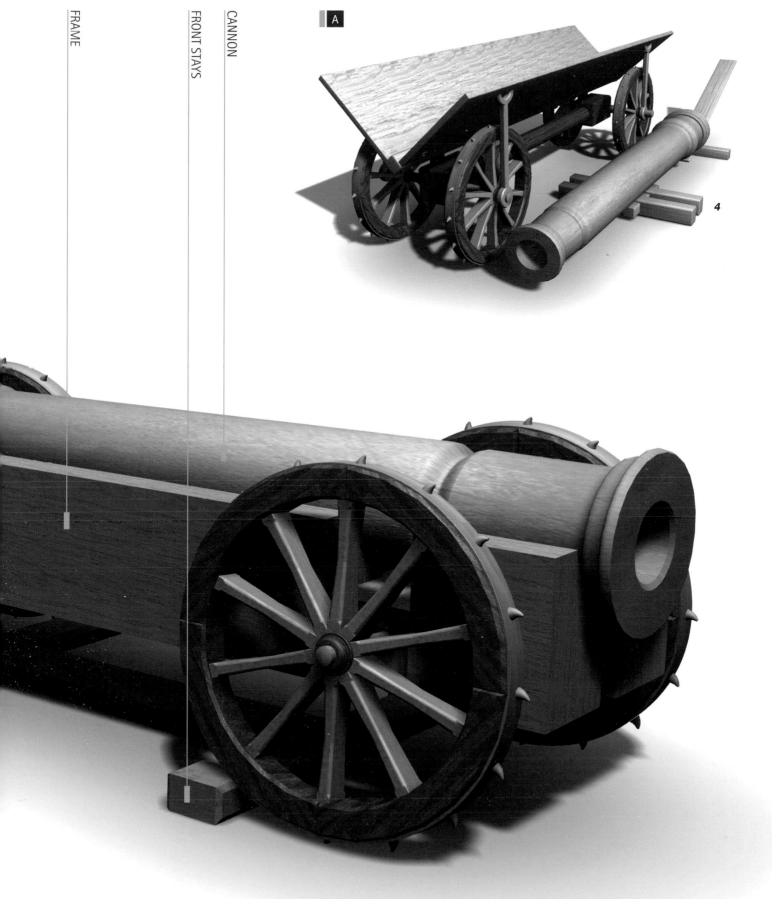

FRAME

FRONT STAYS

CANNON

A

4

Vinci, 1452

1460

1470

1480

circa 1485

1490

1500

1510

Amboise, 1519

1

Armoured Car

2

For Leonardo and his era, both the armoured chariot with rotating scythes and the covered tank armed with a series of cannons, are examples of inventions having classical origins, models to rediscover and emulate. In a note about the scythed chariot Leonardo clearly alludes to this ancient origin: 'These chariots were of various kinds [...]'.

The attitude that Leonardo and the Renaissance artist-engineers had about the classical world, however, is not only one of admiration and imitation, they wanted to emulate and exceed it. The idea of an armoured car with a tortoise-like cover, dating from antiquity, was known since the Middle Ages. Leonardo takes the general idea and freely plays with it, modifying it, integrating it. Just as for painting, sculpture and architecture, the classical model does not suffocate the creativity of the Renaissance artist-engineer, instead, it stimulates it. Thus, Leonardo creates in his imagination an original way to move the tank (using men or animals), and designs a series of cannons mounted around its circumference. From an iconographical point of view, in the drawings for both the armoured tank and the scythed chariot, we are in a dimension that is half way between purely a technological and scientific mechanical representation and a mechanical representation transformed into a dramatic scene. In the two images of the covered tank, Leonardo provides us with an exterior and interior representation of the machine and its structure, its 'anatomy'. In this latter type of image Leonardo gives us information about the gears and the wheels in the drive system. The type of drawing, however, that defines these parts is little more than a sketch, while the right-hand drawing represents the tank not only in its complete form, but also in action on the battlefield with a cloud of projectiles and dust in its wake. Something similar happens in the drawing depicting the scythed chariot. In this case, the definition of the mechanical parts is made using a very clear, decisive drawing. But the dramatic representation of the human and animal figures dominates the image: a horse with his head lowered, the rider suddenly turned to the rear, sensing danger. Movements that fully express the excitement of battle and once more go beyond the naked presentation of simply a mechanical device.

fig. 1
The page contains two drawings; the first shows the mechanisms for moving the car, the second is an armoured car in a most unlikely race across the battlefield.

fig. 2
View of the armoured tank at eye-level.

A

It must be premised that it would have been very difficult for this machine to have crossed over the fields of battle. Leonardo himself writes: 'I will make armoured cars, safe and unassailable, which will enter the close ranks of the enemy with their artillery, and no company of soldiers is so great that they will not break through them. And behind these, the infantry will be able to follow quite unharmed and without any opposition'. The intent behind the project was probably to amaze and shock more than wreak true havoc on the battlefield. In theory, presumably eight men move the machine, manoeuvring the tank and loading the cannons from the inside.

The tank was driven by the activation of cranks and toothed wheels, but the force required to actually move the structure exceeded human power; for this reason the possibility of using horses or oxen was considered, but the presence of these animals in such a closed, restricted space was surely not possible.

B

The tank worked in a very simple manner. Operators turned the central cranks and the wheel began to turn. Once underway, and presuming a perfectly flat terrain, the tank would have made its way over the land. The greatest difficulty was in starting the machine; the scarce amount of available energy and the disproportion between the structure and its entire weight must have been remarkable. The tank was so high that inside ladders were probably used to reach the upper turret; this area was used for sighting and for signalling manoeuvres and artillery operations. The many cannons provided a firing range of 360 degrees.

B

4

fig. 3
Semi-transparent view of the armoured car, where the complex interior structure and the number of parts are visible.

fig. 4
Drive mechanism for the tank, corrected with respect to Leonardo's drawing where an error is made in the working mechanism.

fig. 5
Exploded view and parts of the armoured car.

A

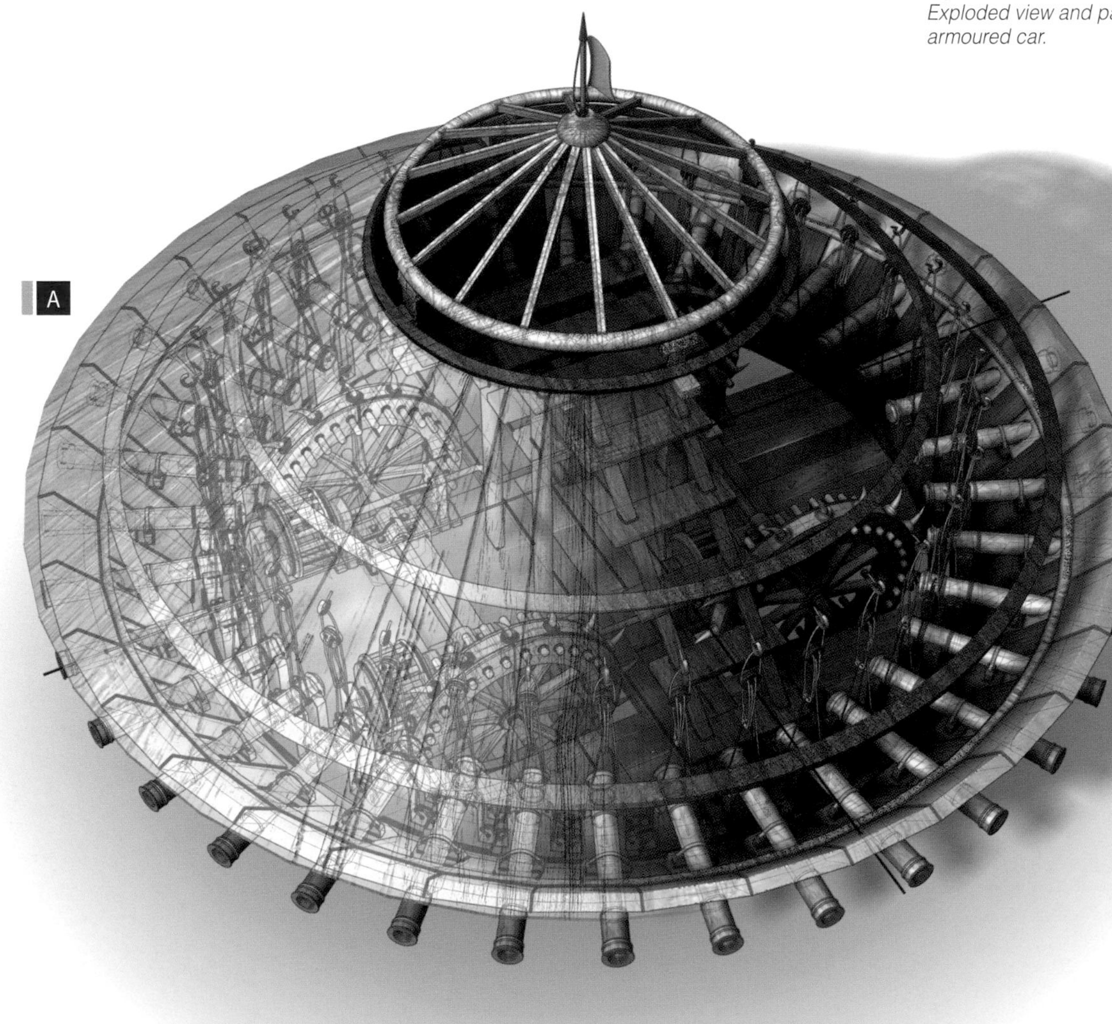

3

SIGHTING TURRET OPEN

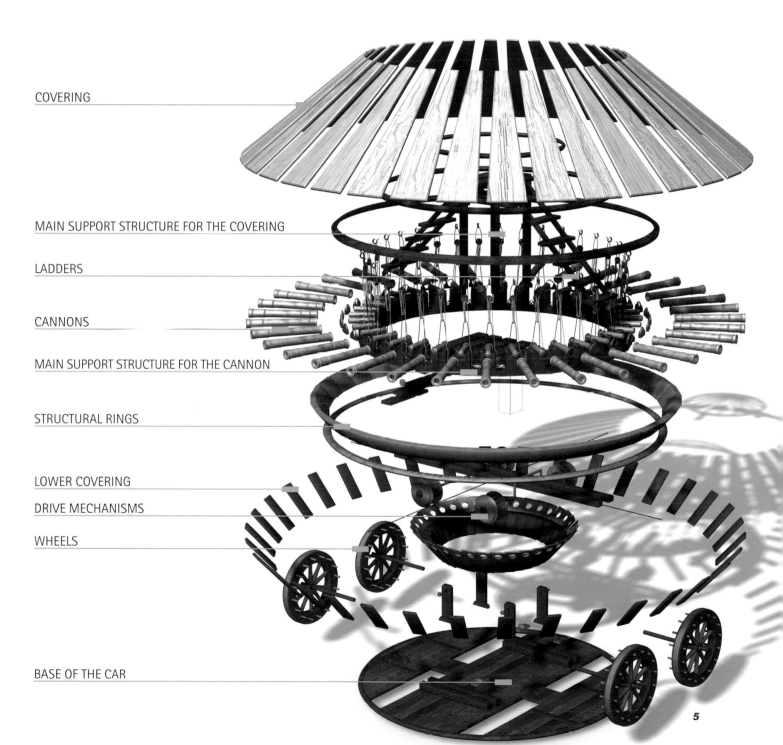

COVERING

MAIN SUPPORT STRUCTURE FOR THE COVERING

LADDERS

CANNONS

MAIN SUPPORT STRUCTURE FOR THE CANNON

STRUCTURAL RINGS

LOWER COVERING

DRIVE MECHANISMS

WHEELS

BASE OF THE CAR

5

Vinci, 1452

1460

1470

1480

1485-1490

1490

1500

1510

Amboise, 1519

Codex Atlanticus, ff. 140ar and 140br

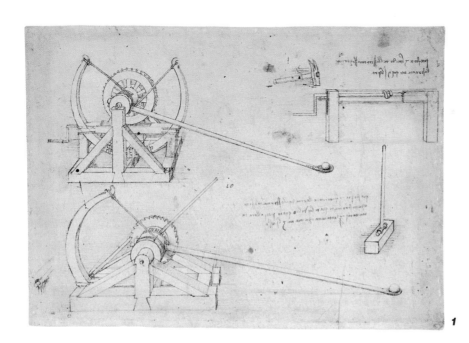

1

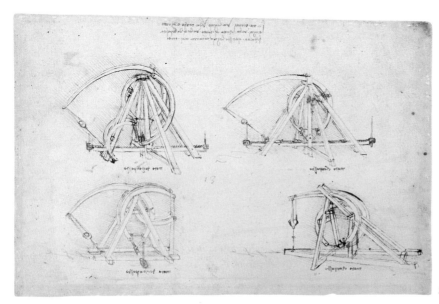

2

Catapult

Leonardo placed the projects for spring catapults together on this page. They date from about 1485-1490 and now are divided into two separate sheets. From a conceptual standpoint they are very interesting, because on one hand they contain elements of Leonardo's early studies, and on the other, elements from the 1490s, the period in which Leonardo attains great equilibrium in many areas of his research, and with very revolutionary solutions.

The content of the drawings has characteristics echoing Leonardo's youthful period: catapults are war machines that are already well known. Still effectively used on the battlefield next to the most innovative firearms, they were essentially objects of humanistic curiosity, having been widely used during the classical era. The antiquarian aspect present in these projects, echoing Leonardo's youthful studies, is surpassed by an intense reflection of the possible variations to it basic workings, the spring propulsion system. In essence, more than just single design projects for catapults, the true topic of thought in these drawings seems to be the spring mechanism itself. This aspect brings the catapult drawings closer to the Da Vincian mechanical masterpiece, the *Treatise on the Elements of Mechanics,* a lost manuscript we know vaguely something about from the studies in the Madrid I manuscript. The most innovative aspect of the treatise was in a section on the study of single, basic mechanisms (the mechanical elements) such as the wheel, the screw, and the spring. It was a fundamental form of theoretical development in mechanical design that was emancipated from the invention of single machines in order to study the basic elements which would be applied to the actual machines themselves. Even the style and the layout of the page reflect this new intellectual dimension where by this point Leonardo is designing mechanical inventions. In the lost *Treatise on the Elements of Mechanics,* next to the theoretical sections, a more practical part was planned where the laws of mechanics and the various elements (wheels, springs, etc.) were applied to the construction of the specific machines. The folio here furnishes us with an idea of how this part of the treatise might have been, and in particular the illustration of the spring applied to war machines.

3

figs. 1 and 2
Two pages illustrating different projects for catapults that function on energy released from curved wood.

fig. 3
The catapult in the launch phase.

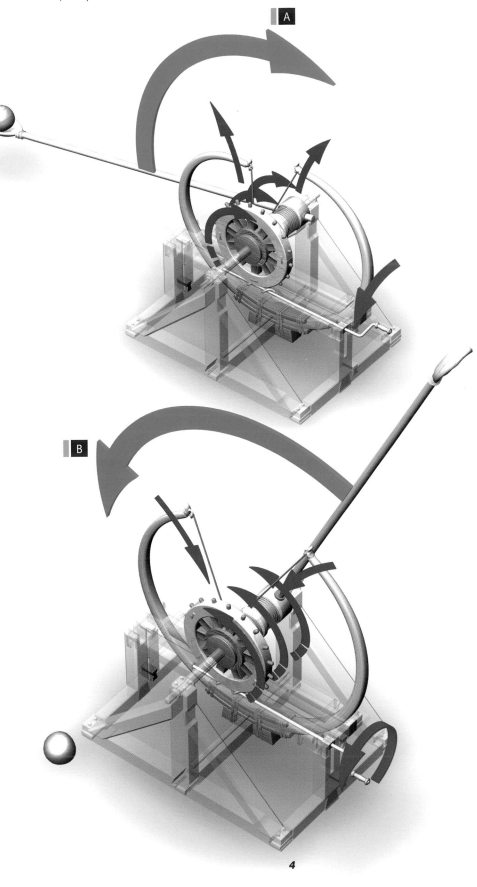

A The catapult had a considerable firing range and was therefore used for targets even very far away. In this project, Leonardo tries to increase the power and the practicality of this wartime tool. The two large leaf springs, presumably constructed in bent wood, ensured a very powerful thrust. When the leaf spring was loaded the two wooden arms were tensioned, curving back on themselves. Then, a weight was carefully placed in the spoon, and when everything was ready for the launch the operator only had to give a forceful turn to the front crank. When the mechanism freed the two bows, these suddenly returned to their resting position, releasing the lever and hurling the stone; these devices could also hurl incendiary projectiles.

B Once the launch operations were concluded, the catapult could be quickly reloaded. The operator who released the shot, turned the crank causing the two wooden bows to curve, closing up on themselves. Leonardo had also designed a self-blocking system for the reloading operations. Due to the fact that the springs were very rigid the loading operation could not be done using only the hand crank. It would have certainly snapped under the excessive strain. The toothed wheel on the inside most probably concealed one or more ratchet wheels, which blocked the movement of the bows while the catapult was being loaded. The loading operation was accompanied by the typical clicking sound of the ratchet. The amount of energy released was so forceful that the frame had to be anchored to the ground using lines and stakes.

fig. 4
Illustration of the various phases of launching and loading; the mechanism was very simple and the leaf spring could easily make repeated launches in a short period of time.

fig. 5
Illustration of the parts during launch.

**following pages,
fig. 6**
Representation of a possible attack on an enemy castle.

4

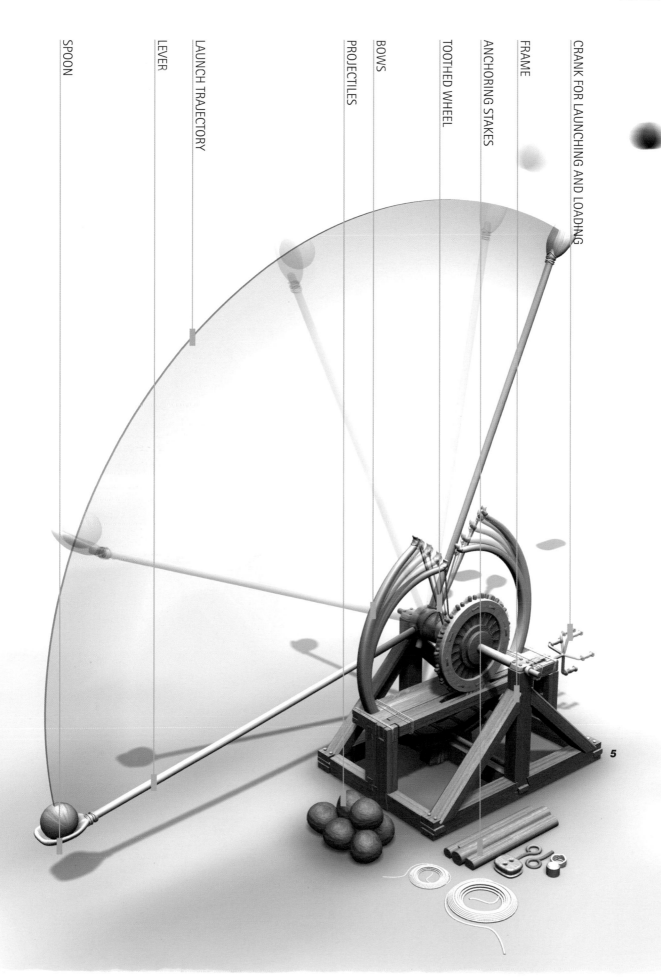

SPOON

LEVER

LAUNCH TRAJECTORY

PROJECTILES

BOWS

TOOTHED WHEEL

ANCHORING STAKES

FRAME

CRANK FOR LAUNCHING AND LOADING

5

Vinci, 1452

1460

1470

1480

1490

1500

1503-1505

1510

Amboise, 1519

Codex Atlanticus, f. 1ar

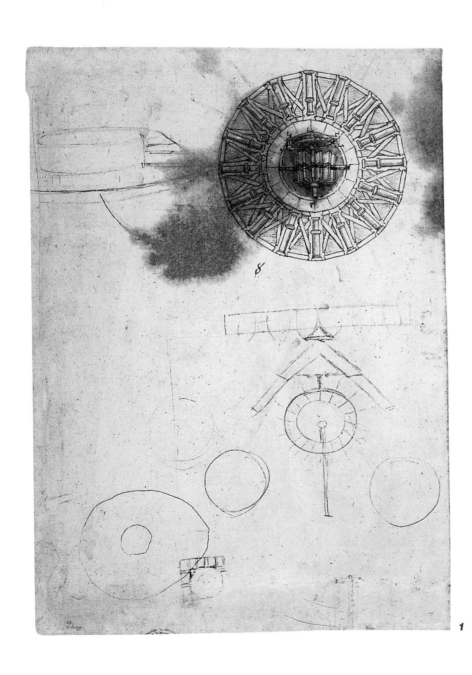

1

Barrage Cannon

2

This folio is part of the Codex Atlanticus, a collection of sheets put together not by Leonardo, but after his death at the end of the sixteenth century. In the upper corner, Leonardo has created a magnificent drawing of an 'encircling thunderbolt', the same term he used to describe another, very similar device found in Manuscript B. This 'circular-lightning' device is a multiple-barrelled bombard with the gun muzzles positioned around a circular platform. It is a well-finished drawing that is the culmination of previous ideas and sketches, laid out as we might say, in good copy. The pen defines the shape of the various forms using a precise, decided line. Then, this line drawing is completed with hatching and an ink wash. It is evident that the lines are made by a left-handed artist, as seen by the way that they slant. By following their direction we perceive that during the hatching process, Leonardo continually rotated the sheet of paper. The ink wash is used to highlight the volume of the cannons. It is not possible to firmly date this drawing. A similar, but much simpler, 'circular-lightning' device is shown on a warship in a drawing in Manuscript B dating from about 1485-1489. But this drawing does not have Leonardo's same regular, filiform character typical of that period. Instead, it has the force and content reminiscent of the years during work on the *Battle of Anghiari*, around 1504. The well-finished character of this drawing did not, however, seem to find great fortune. At a certain point various unrelated sketches were inserted onto the page, only one of which (an architectural subject) can be attributed to Leonardo.

This drawing has a force that goes beyond its mechanical content. Leonardo chooses to present the weapon from a very high vantage point, perpendicular to and overlooking the machine itself. It is almost a plot drawing that does not sacrifice, however, the detail and strength in the forms that make up the machine. The hatching and the ink wash serve to regain the sense of volume in the forms that a plot drawing tends to flatten. At the same time, the drawing has the crystalline clarity of a geometric diagram (a circle scanned by a series of rays and diagonals), and the force evocative of a real structure. The forms of the cannon and the structures that hinge them together create a percussive visual cadence. The workings of the machine, the series of shots fired from these cannons seem to be transfigured into image, from ballistic rhythm to visual rhythm. Only many years later towards the middle of the sixteenth century, Michelangelo will create forms on the tambour of the cupola of St Peter's capable of evoking this rhythm with this much force.

fig. 1
This project for a barrage cannon is drawn on the first page of the Codex Atlanticus; the most well-known and striking drawing is in the upper right corner, but a few less-visible lines in the same drawing conceal secrets and information that open the doors to many different interpretations.

fig. 2
An overhead view of the machine exactly as it appears on the Leonardo's page.

2

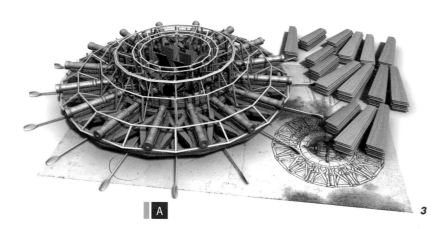

A

3

A On the upper right side of the page Leonardo presents a clear and distinct drawing, however, there are many barely sketched out drawings on the same page that open the way to a variety of interpretations. Historically, it has always been hypothesised that this giant structure was a sort of bombard that could be positioned on top of a tower, or on a land-bound civil structure. Under careful analysis, a sort of probable covering can be discerned, incoherent with the machine's interpretation. There also appear to be double lines close to all the construction rays in the main drawing. One of the possible interpretations for these faint but clear marks is that they represent oars for manoeuvring the machine on water. Its use on water would also furnish a coherent explanation of the central mechanism, the paddle wheels, an element for which it would be difficult to logically place the device on top of a tower. Difficulties in this placement would have also been encountered considering the weight and construction limitations imposed by the work. Nonetheless, it must be remembered that the barrage cannon on water is still only one of the possible interpretations for this project.

B The sequence illustrates the different phases in assembling the bombard. The cannons are positioned and fixed to a sturdy frame. Before Leonardo places on the covering, sketched in the upper left of the manuscript, he constructs the frame. Below, the barrage cannon as it must have appeared after the construction was completed.

B

figs. 2, 3 and 4
*The sequence for assembling the entire structure,
following the indications suggested by the faint
sketch in the upper part of the manuscript.*

fig. 5
*An exploded view of a section of the bombard.
It takes sixteen sections to construct
the entire weapon.*

GANGWAY

LOADING HATCH

CANNON

CANNON HOUSING

SUPPORT FRAME

SECTION EDGE

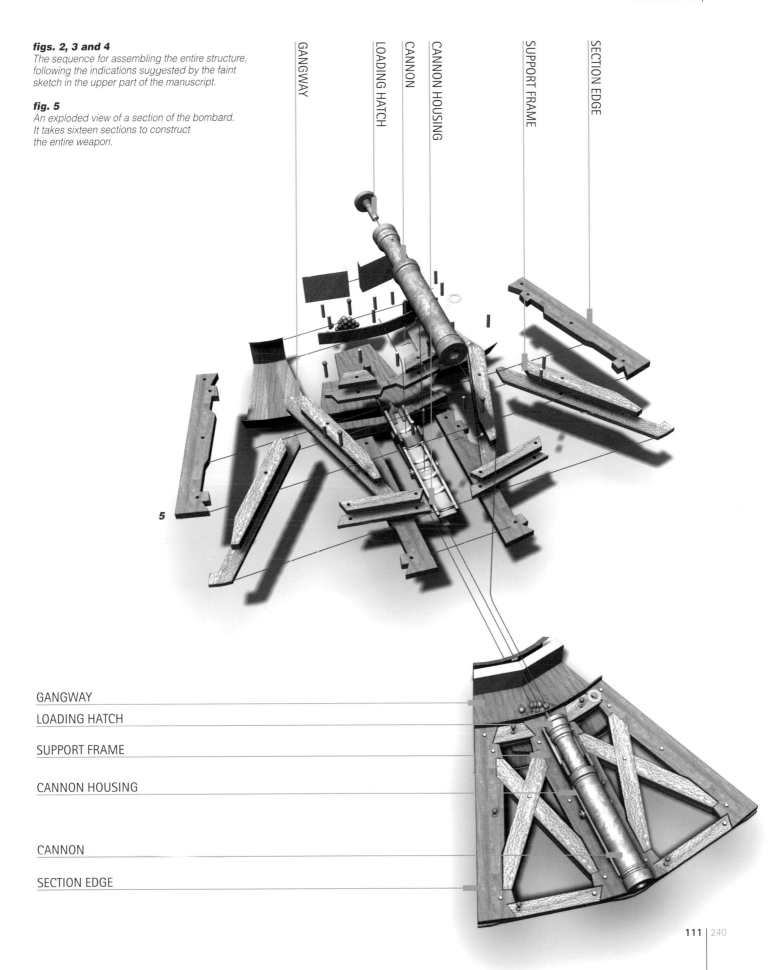

5

GANGWAY

LOADING HATCH

SUPPORT FRAME

CANNON HOUSING

CANNON

SECTION EDGE

A The aquatic interpretation of the machine probably presents the most interesting aspect; its use on water explains the internal mechanisms that Leonardo designed for movement and manoeuvrability. By using a system similar to that for boats powered by paddles, the barrage cannon, which must have been very heavy, could navigate in a straight line in the water but could also manoeuvre with a fair amount of agility. The vessel could also turn around on itself; this manoeuvre simply required that one of the operators stopped turning his paddle, or that both paddle wheels turned in the opposite direction.

B Two operators moved the large drive wheel, and by turning the cranks the vessel began to move; this operation was not that easy because of the enormous weight and the inertia of the entire structure; the wheel and the crank would have broken. Leonardo comes up with a gear reduction system that can slowly begin the motion for the entire machine. He designs two smaller cranks that turn two small cage-shaped gears. Once the motion was begun, the water resistance diminished and the operators could move to the larger wheel and continue the movement directly with this. This geared shield or barrage cannon could even reach considerable speeds for its size and bulk.

figs. 6 and 7
An exploded view of the motor mechanism, and, the system assembled. The interpretation of this device is the most interesting aspect of the entire machine.

fig. 8
How the finished machine must have looked, ready for navigation.

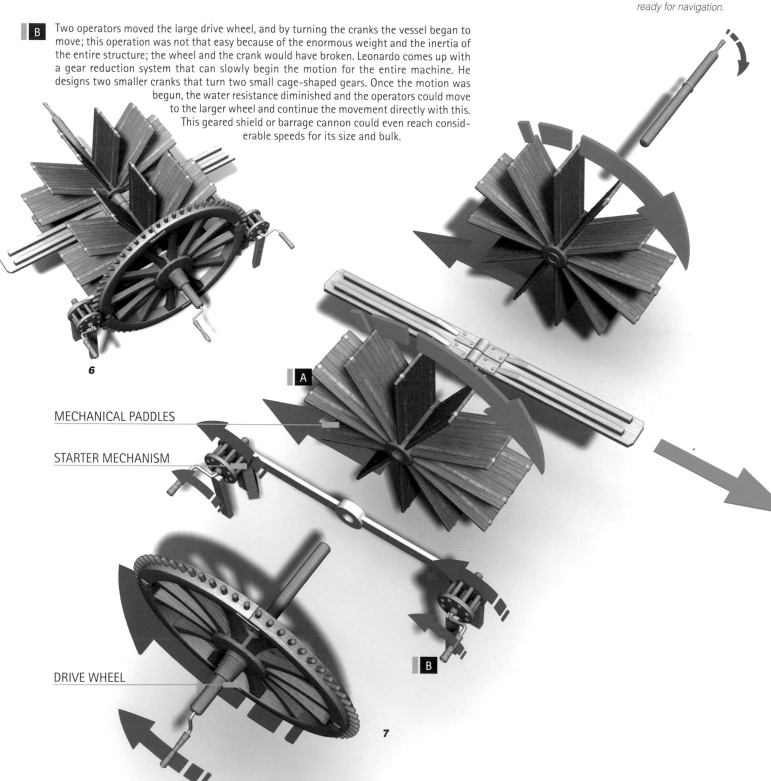

6

A

MECHANICAL PADDLES

STARTER MECHANISM

B

DRIVE WHEEL

7

fig. 9

An exploded view of all the parts in the bombard-shield. The construction and launching onto the water must have been long and expensive undertakings, both in terms of human labour and in obtaining the materials: the wood, but especially the metal for the cannons.

**following pages,
fig. 10**

Leonardo himself appears aboard the bombard on its maiden voyage; it is almost certain that the machine was never actually made.

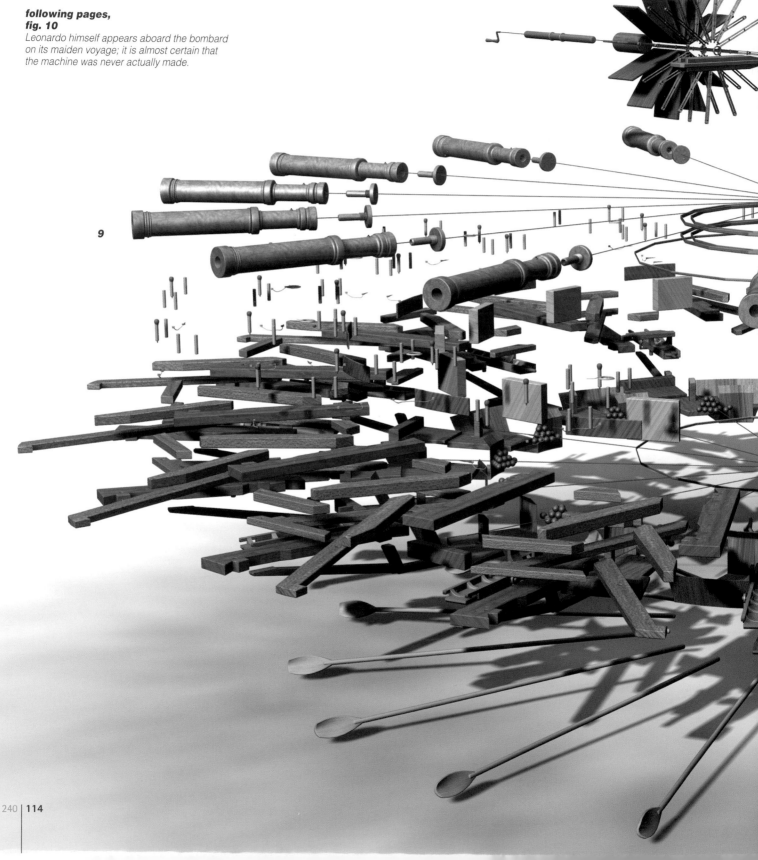

9

Vinci, 1452

1460

1470

1480

1490

1500

circa 1504

1510

Amboise, 1519

Codex Atlanticus, f. 33r

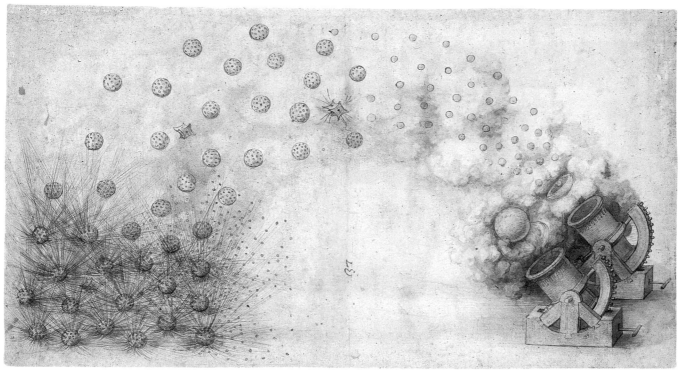

1

Bombards in action

This page from the Codex Atlanticus is not one of Leonardo's personal studies, but rather a presentation study for a patron. The very-finished style of the drawing and its technical complexity, making use of a pen and ink base drawing gone over with ink wash, together with the absence of written notes, all confirm this image's intended use. In presentation drawings often Leonardo either completely eliminates written notes or includes them in normal, left to right handwriting to ensure easy reading by others. Leonardo was not the only one to use technical drawings as presentation images. With these and other drawings of machines, Leonardo followed in the tradition of the *Quattrocento* engineers. The manuscripts of Leonardo's two predecessors, Francesco di Giorgio and Mariano di Jacopo called 'il Taccola', were certainly not workshop manuals but rather refined collections of images and notes (also in Latin) destined for a cultured reading public. We do not know for whom this drawing of bombards with exploding hailshot was destined. Additionally, the page can not be easily dated. Its striking character brings to mind Leonardo's early years; the clear layout of the project puts us in the 1490s, period when Leonardo undertakes remarkable studies on ballistics. The stylistic characteristics, however, place us in the early 1500s when Leonardo is working as military engineer on various battlefronts (in the entourage of Cesare Borgia in Romagna, and in Tuscany for the Florentine Republic).

An intrinsically important element links this drawing to some studies on bombards in action dating from about 1504 (Windsor Castle, no. 12275 and Codex Atlanticus, f. 72r): there is an artistic transformation to the ballistic aspects of bombards in these projects. In fact, the drawing is centred around the parabolic path described by the shots in their entirety, and especially (on the left side of the page) on the range and extension of each single shell after it explodes and the shells as a whole. Rather than just the exploded fragments of each shot, a very fine halo of lines is used to define these effects. In defining these lines of force, we perceive the awareness of a scientist who obstinately worked at grasping the laws of ballistics by studying the interference of the air. But at the same time the filiform, taut rays also become images of incomparable aesthetic beauty. These mechanical drawings are to Leonardo's studies on ballistics just as the sublime drawings of Floods are to his studies on hydrology: the lucid obsession with a scientific law that coincides with the creation of an artistic image, an event that to date in the history of man, only Leonardo has achieved with such comprehensiveness.

fig. 1
The drawing by Leonardo on folio 33r in the Codex Atlanticus.

fig. 2
Some projectile fragments.

A The bombard was a weapon already known at the time of Leonardo. The truly interesting aspects of this project are essentially the quality of the drawing, of unmistakable clarity, illustrating the bombards in action, and the studies in projectile fragmentation. Otherwise, the bombard drawn on the page does not contain any particular innovations; it was necessarily constructed of a sturdy base because of the great amount of energy released by the explosion upon firing. The bombard was most probably anchored to the terrain using stakes and lines.

The bombard had a single direction of fire, and the operator could regulate only the elevation of the shot. The direction of the shot depended exclusively on the position of the base, and because this was fastened to the ground it was difficult to move. There were probably a number of bombards positioned across a hypothetical battlefield in order to cover a greater attack area.

B The firing elevation could be easily adjusted by turning a crank; when the crank was turned, the operator could regulate the shot with great precision. The crank activated a metallic rod with a worm screw; the screw engaged the teeth in the toothed semiarc and the bombard moved up and down. Precision in this phase was of utmost importance; first of all with the short, stumpy barrel the shot trajectory was already fairly imprecise, and also because in a long-range shot even a few degrees variance made a big difference in its length.

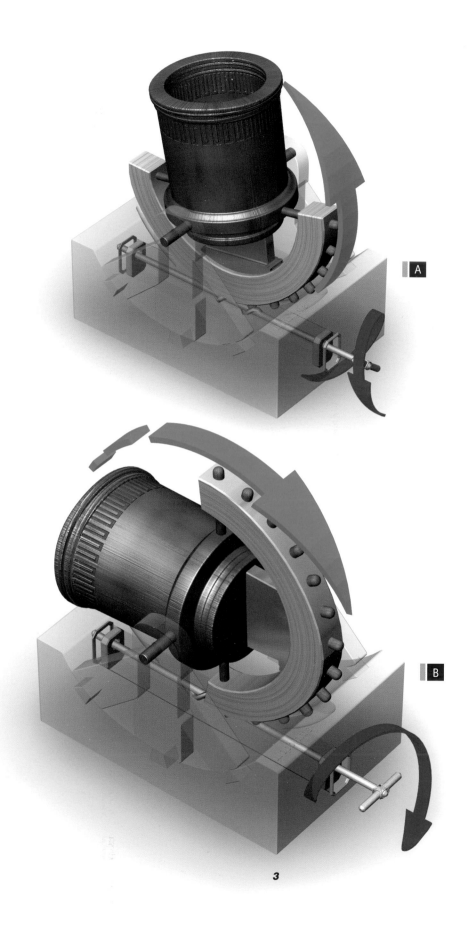

A

B

3

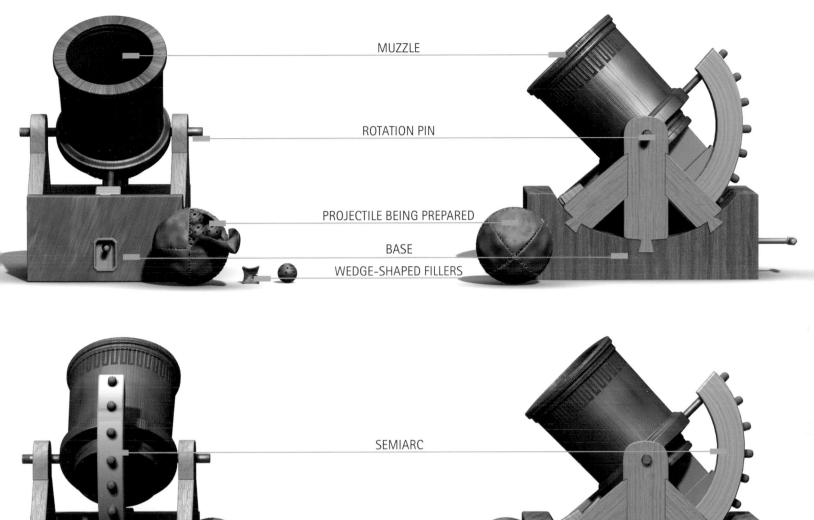

MUZZLE

ROTATION PIN

PROJECTILE BEING PREPARED

BASE

WEDGE-SHAPED FILLERS

SEMIARC

FRAME

CRANK

4

fig. 3
*Diagram of the functioning and adjustment
of firing elevation.*

fig. 4
Orthogonal views and description of the parts.

**overleaf,
figs. 5 and 6**
Exploded views of the bombard and hailshot.

A Visualisation of the internal parts of an exploding cannonball: along with the mini-gun-powder shot there were wedge-shaped iron pieces that kept the round shot together inside the shell. Leonardo's packing system was not the most effective, but during that period, without specific drafting tools it was difficult to represent and imagine other solutions.

B Once all the internal parts were assembled, the cannonballs were stitched up by joining the petal-shaped pieces together.

C Sewing the cannonballs was done by hand and it required precision and attention. The final sewing operation consisted in joining together the top part connecting all the pieces.

D Once the stitching was finished, the cannonball was ready to be loaded into the barrel of the bombard.

E Exploded view of the bombard. In this image it is important to note the complex structure of the weapon and some of it functional characteristics, for example the worm screw, used to adjust the inclination of the barrel that is worked by turning a rear crank.

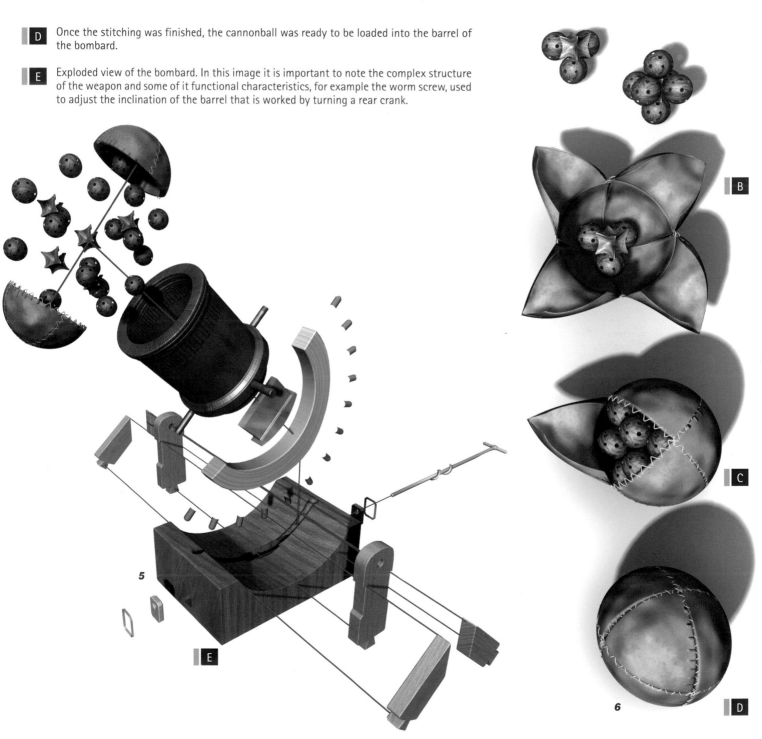

overleaf,
fig. 7
A view of the bombard in firing position.

fig. 8
The bombard placed on top of the folio faithfully replicates its position in Leonardo's drawing, leaving no space for other interpretations.

BASE

MUZZLE

CANNONBALL READY FOR FIRING

FRAME

PROJECTILE BEING PREPARED

HAILSHOT

WEDGE-SHAPED FILLERS

ROTATION PIN

BARREL

SEMIARC

CRANK

TIE HOOKS

TIE LINES

8

Vinci, 1452

1460

1470

1480

1490

1500

1507-1510

1510

Amboise, 1519

Codex Atlanticus, f. 117r

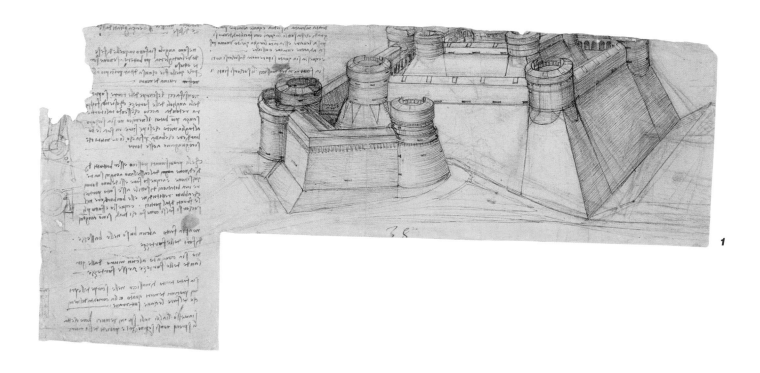

1

Fortress

2

The drawing of a fortress on this page in the Codex Atlanticus dates to the period of Leonardo's second sojourn in Milan, from about 1508. The political scene has changed radically, and now with the expulsion of the Sforza, the French have taken control. Having worked previously for the Sforza, Leonardo now receives important commissions from the French government. In fact, he is named 'ingénieur ordinaire', and probably the study for the fortress on this page was realised for the French, in an era when the need to militarily safeguard one's conquests was ever more pressing. It was not the first time Leonardo undertook military problems. Aside from some probable minor commissions from the Sforza, Leonardo had acted as consultant in this field for the Venetian authorities, and shortly after, he followed Cesare Borgia on his campaign for the conquest of the Romagna region. Just prior to his commitment with Cesare Borgia (in 1502, immediately before his artistic undertaking on a theme dealing with warfare for the *Battle of Anghiari*), in a very systematic fashion he had addressed the important innovation in warfare of the period: firearms. He made ballistic studies, firearm designs, and from a defensive standpoint, he elaborated projects for fortresses and towers having a flattened form with a receding profile, offering a minimal surface area for enemy fire. The project for a fortress developed in these later years is contradictory in character. On one hand, Leonardo applied some of the new, innovative architectural solutions he elaborated in previous years; for example, the profile of some keeps corresponds to this concept. At the same time however, the fortress has almost a medieval majesty about it and in his plan polygonal perimeters prevail. Initially Leonardo gives a curved, outwardly convex movement to the ravelin (the wall outside the main gate). He changes this idea, giving this part of the fortress a polygonal, angled shape. This was the form preferred by Francesco di Giorgio in his many fortresses designed and built in various parts of Italy. It is possible that he may have influenced Leonardo. Immediately after 1500, Leonardo had the opportunity to study a copy of the *Treatise on Architecture* by Francesco di Giorgio, upon which he even inserts some of his own notes. It is also possible that the layout of the fortress using innovative but less revolutionary forms was an explicit request by the patrons.

fig. 1
Folio with a clear drawing of the fortress and some annotations that recount a true incident regarding military treachery.

fig. 2
A view of the plan of the fortress.

A

This fortress was probably designed for a mountainous area; perched on to top of a mountain or hill, the dimensions and distinctive shape of the walls rendered the fortress practically storm-proof. The surrounding walls defend the central portion of the complex where the lord of the castle lived. About the mid-1400s the use of gunpowder and firearms was developed and all the systems of defence including the castle walls had to adjust to this new type of attack. Leonardo designs walls where the relationship between the layout and the vertical section of the walls is noticeably augmented. With this type of profile the walls, having increased structural consistency, can absorb the blasts of the new offensive weapons. The other innovation introduced into the project is the absence of traditional battlements: the profile of the walls becomes a rounded curve that can deflect the impact of cannon fire; small openings allow the defenders to keep the situation under control and respond to the firepower.

B

The geometrical configuration of the entire fortress is interesting, and very carefully planned. Believing the walls to be insuperable, Leonardo does not worry about covering one side of the fortress with natural structures such as slopes or ditches; on the contrary, he tries to free-up the perimeter of the castle, not so much to protect it as to cut off an easy escape. Once the enemy realised that the fortress could not be attacked, there would not be even a sheltered path of retreat.

fig. 3
The fortress was so imposing and inaccessible that any offensive initiative would have been in vain.

3

128

TOWERS

PARAPET

PLAN OF THE WALLS

CENTRAL KEEP

LORD'S QUARTERS

INTERNAL PERIMETER

ENTRANCE

A

B

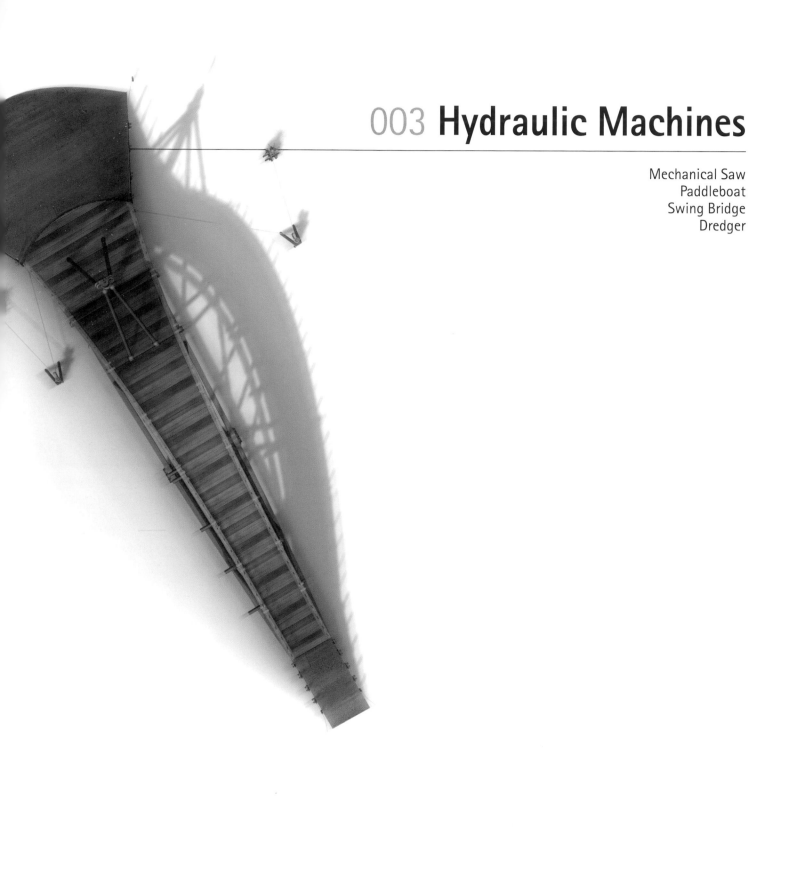

003 **Hydraulic Machines**

Mechanical Saw
Paddleboat
Swing Bridge
Dredger

Leonardo often combined his study of water with air, designing both hydraulic machines and flying machines. He studies the waves on the sea to indirectly grasp the behaviour of the air, and some of his flying machines are reminiscent in both form and mechanical concept to boats (Codex Atlanticus, f. 156r and 860r). Still, from other points of view, the two areas are very distant from one another. The projects for the flying machine are totally part of Leonardo's private world: in fact, we have no evidence to hypothesise that any of his clients took interest in this realm of Leonardo's creativity. Our impression is that Leonardo tends to keep secret this side of his inventive activity. Hydraulic engineering is perhaps the field where Leonardo pursues his most on-going work, not only in his personal study but also in actual projects, important commissions from rulers in the various places where he lives.

Vasari informs us that still in his youth, during the first period in Florence, Leonardo is consulted on a problem of public interest: how to render navigable the Arno River from Florence to the sea. 'And while he was still young, he was the first to propose making the Arno into a navigable canal between Pisa and Florence'. It is easily understood why hydraulic engineering would be the field in which Leonardo most closely worked with patrons (and in this sense, only partially equalled by military engineering). In addition to supplying a basic element to the cities and using it as a driving force for various types of machines, during Leonardo's day water was the fastest means of commercial transportation. Leonardo found himself working in two centres – Florence and Milan – both far from the sea, the main navigable body of water. In both centres everything imaginable was attempted, using creativity and riches, to overcome this obstacle. Leonardo participates in trying to resolve these problems, an on-going challenge for generations of engineers. On one hand, he demonstrates interest for solutions already attempted or implemented, while on the other, he proposes new solutions. In Milan, the canal system of the Navigli used very advanced solutions, solutions from which Leonardo would greatly benefit. The same was true for Florence: Filippo Brunelleschi had already approached the problem of navigating the Arno, although with little success. He designed a strange, large boat – the so-called 'Badalone' (vagabond). Brunelleschi's intent was that it be capable of transporting heavy marble blocks from the quarries near the sea to Florence. We have no drawings by the young Leonardo relating to this problem, however, according to one hypothesis the drawing on the folio 90v in the Codex Atlanticus, with its system of locks along a canal, could hint at the early project that Vasari mentions. We possess other drawings from Leonardo's early years relative to hydraulic problems, and especially, drawings of mechanical devices in the Codex Atlanticus for lifting water, the most famous of which is the so-called Archimedean screw (a screw or an arrangement of blades sealed inside a cylinder that when properly inclined, drained water). Again in this case, Leonardo makes reference to what had already been invented by the Tuscan engineers. He studies and analyses solutions from a highly regarded tradition and at the same time begins to move away from it. As a result, designing hydraulic machines is an activity Leonardo increasingly ties to his studies on the physical and dynamic behaviour of water as an element in and of itself, and in its relation to other elements. In his studies from the later years in Florence, and just after his transfer to Milan (1482-1483), he is already attracted by the analogies between water and air. He studies animals that seem to belong to both these elements, such as the flying fish, from where he takes the idea for membrane-covered wings suitable for flying as well as swimming (the webbed gloves drawn on folio 81v in Manuscript B, circa 1486-1489). Aside from this more scientific theoretical elaboration (still immature for the moment), in this period Leonardo also goes beyond practical application, giving full rein to his imagination in designing a submarine and a complex system for attacking enemy ships by breaching the hull underwater (Manuscript B, f. 81v and Codex Atlanticus, f. 881r).

A few years later in 1500, Leonardo is once again caught up with design in a concrete context when he hastily leaves Milan in 1499 to spend some time in Venice. In fact, the 'Serenissma' Republic commissions him to come up with an effective system of defence for its eastern confines, under constant threat from the Ottoman advance. Leonardo designs a defence system using palisades on the river Isonzo (Codex Atlanticus, ff. 638dv, 215r). In working on his projects, Leonardo often takes their public dimension into consideration, as we deduce from a folio (Windsor 12680) where Leonardo has delineated the course of the Arno river in the vicinity of Florence, indicating a chain system intended to stem the flow of the river and that damaged the riverbanks. The notations that accompany the drawing are not in his backwards handwriting so often found on his pages, but in the normal sense from left to right, a sign that these studies could have been seen by clients. Leonardo returns to Florence (we are in the early 1500s) and the authorities of the Republic involve him in at least three large hydraulic engineering projects: the on-going problem of rendering the Arno navigable from Florence to the sea, the project where the course of the Arno is deviated to leave the rebellious Pisa without water (and as in Venice, he combines hydraulic and military engineering), and finally, the attempt to better contain the course of the Arno in the section of the river near Florence.

After 1508 when Leonardo returns to Milan, now under French occupation, he becomes 'peintre et ingénieur ordinaire' to the King of France. In addition to other tasks, he is assigned to design a navigable canal connecting Milan to the northern territories along the Adda River (not navigable in its entire course). For all these commissions, Leonardo designs various contrivances and hydraulic machines, all more or less original and all more or less practicable. It is during these years (about 1508-1510), and in the sphere of his personal studies that the designs of hydraulic machines and devices reach very interesting results. These studies are contained in the Codex Leicester and in Manuscript F. Personal studies are not always free from practical problems. Often the two dimensions are parallel to each other, and by their co-presence constitute one of the most interesting elements in Leonardo's work.

The perfect example of this co-ordination is in a series of notes and drawings where Leonardo constantly goes from a practical problem (the invention of machines for draining a pond) to a series of more theoretical and experimental reflections. In Manuscript F (ff. 13v and 15r), he designs a machine for eliminating water from a pond using a centrifuge activated by wheels (hydraulic wheels, moved by the water in a river, or mounted on a boat, turned by animals); the water is sucked up as a result of the whirlpools that are formed. The idea behind this kind of device implies a theoretical study of the formation of whirlpools and their behaviour. At this point, Leonardo moves on to designing of the centrifuges to be used in theoretical experiments. He creates machines for study that when placed in water create a whirlpool. On folio 16r in Manuscript F Leonardo defines them as 'artificial vortices'. Thus we are dealing with experimental hydraulic machines, a dimension that will later become a foundation in the scientific revolution when alongside his studies Galileo Galilei sets up a workshop to produce instruments, machines of fundamental support in research.

During the final years of his career – between Rome (1513-1516) and France (1517-1519) – Leonardo continues to receive prestigious commissions related to hydraulic engineering as well as occasions for mechanical design. In Rome he is involved in the land reclamation scheme for the Pontine Marshes (Windsor 12684) and he also works on projects for the port of Civitavecchia. A group of pages from his period in France (Codex Atlanticus, ff. 69br, 574, 790r, 810r, 1016r) include inventions for a complex hydraulic system related to a fountain, probably meant for a grandiose pageant at Romorantin for the King of France, Francis I, Leonardo's patron during his later life.

Vinci, 1452

1460

1470

circa 1478

1480

1490

1500

1510

Amboise, 1519

Codex Atlanticus, f. 1078ar

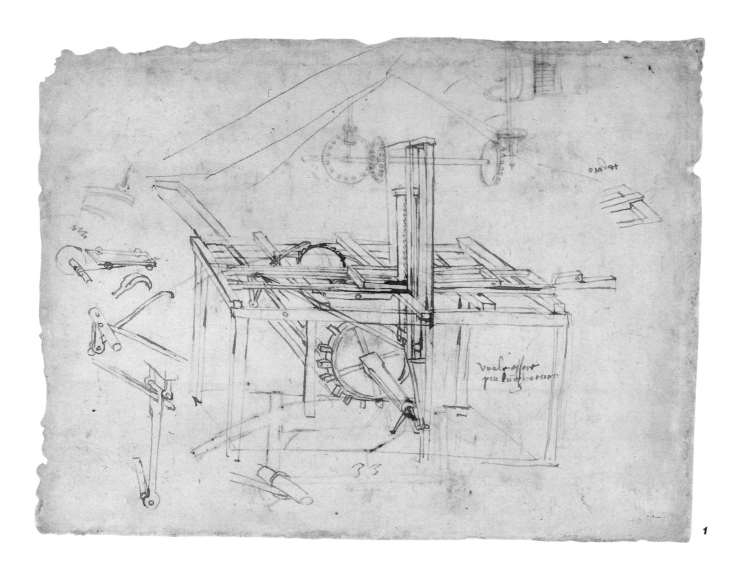

Mechanical Saw

In the mixed collection of sheets known as the Codex Atlanticus, mechanical drawings of inferior quality occasionally appear. It would be difficult to recognise Leonardo's hand in these drawings if they were not next to notes or other unmistakably autograph drawings. The drawing of the mechanical saw on this folio is an example. The pen and ink line delineating the frame for the mechanism is in a very laboured style. Rather than inventing, the individual responsible for this drawing seems to be copying, placing one line after another as if to record an image of either a real machine or the drawing of one. The second hypothesis is the most plausible, especially if we attribute this drawing to Leonardo. In fact, the perspective is approximate and obsolete, reminiscent of drawings for machines of most of the *Quattrocento* engineers. These older images were meant to give a general idea of the machine, using visual conventions that glossed over correct perspective and spatial representation. Simply leafing through the treatises of an author like Mariano di Jacopo, called 'il Taccola', we find many mechanical drawings similar to this one in the Codex Atlanticus. The hypothesis that this drawing is a copy (with eventual modifications) of a device already in use during Leonardo's time and that it is made from a drawing, is backed by the presence of a similar machine in the manuscript conserved in Venice by Lorenzo and Benvenuto della Golpaja, two well-known engineers of that period. As already implied, its attribution to Leonardo is not based so much on its graphic or conceptual quality but rather on its context. In fact, in the upper right there is a detail of the machine accompanied by the annotation 'telaio' (frame) written backwards, in Leonardo's typical handwriting. On the verso of the folio (1078av) there is a drawing, barely more than a sketch, that has the sureness of line found in drawings firmly attributed to Leonardo. The legible note on the project for the saw, 'Vuole essere più lungo tutto' (Everything should be longer) perhaps indicating a modification to the design, is written normally from left to right, as appears when Leonardo wants to share the drawing with someone. It also could be a note by someone other than Leonardo. Further, on a fragment of paper originally part of the page with the mechanical saw (folio 1078bv), there are drawings of Brunelleschian-type turnbuckles (mechanisms used by Brunelleschi for the dome of Santa Maria del Fiore and also copied by other engineers), perhaps drawn by Leonardo as well as letters and flourishes in a handwriting that does not belong to Leonardo. The nature of and the interest in this project are clear: it is a typical study made during his initial years of research before the period of innovation, and together with another young colleague Leonardo studies the great traditions that preceded him.

fig. 1
Folio 1078ar in the Codex Atlanticus.

fig. 2
The mechanical saw on top of the folio in fig. 1.

2

A Upper carriage pulls the tree-trunk to be cut, by running along a track in the same direction as the cut and passing over the saw blade.

B System of pulleys attached to a crankshaft that automatically and gradually moves the upper carriage while the wood is being cut.

C Waterwheel that uses water in a small channel below the machine. A rotatory motion produces the mechanical energy transferred by various phases to the cutting device above.

fig. 3
View of the mechanical hydraulic saw as conceived by Leonardo. The structural elements are in transparency; the cutting device and the waterwheel mechanism that transfers the energy to the cutting mechanism are highlighted.

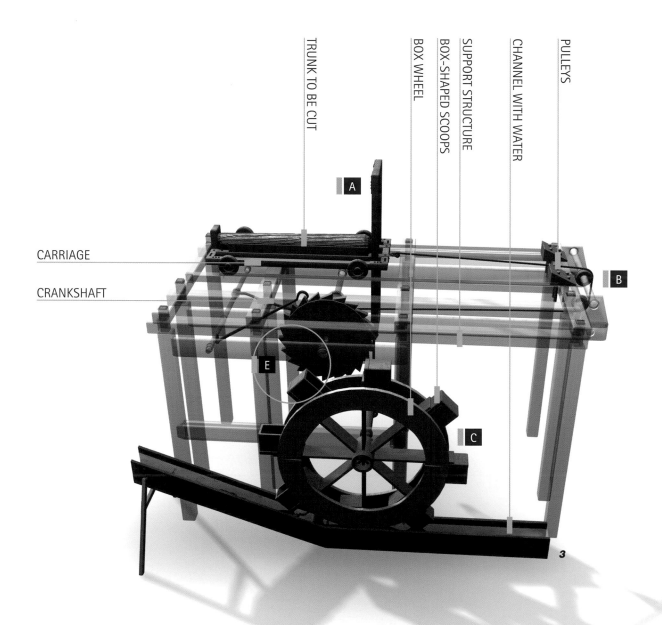

TRUNK TO BE CUT

BOX WHEEL

BOX-SHAPED SCOOPS

SUPPORT STRUCTURE

CHANNEL WITH WATER

PULLEYS

CARRIAGE

CRANKSHAFT

fig. 4
*Front view of the saw showing the mechanism
that transforms continuous rotary motion
into reciprocating linear motion
(the up and down sawing motion).*

fig. 5
Diagram of the workings of the hydraulic saw.

D The wheel with box-shaped scoops is put in motion by the running water in the channel below.
The turning axles transfer the energy produced by rotatory motion to the other mechanisms.

E This mechanism transforms the hydraulic rotatory motion into the energy necessary to work the system of pulleys and crankshafts that pull the carriage with the tree-trunk, keeping it moving at a constant speed in the direction of the cut.

F This phase transforms the original continuous rotary motion to linear reciprocating motion allowing the saw to make the up and down cut. A line governed by a pulley system is tied to the upper carriage and it pulls it along the frame to the saw blade.

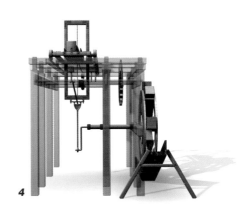

4

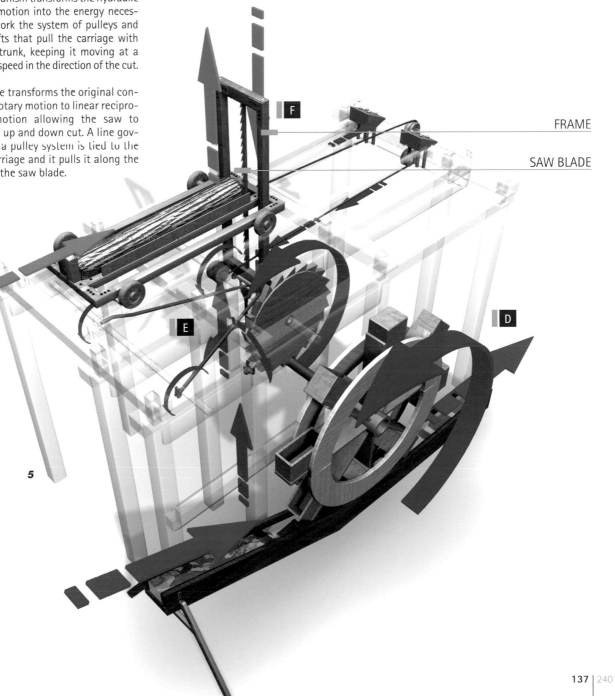

FRAME

SAW BLADE

5

6

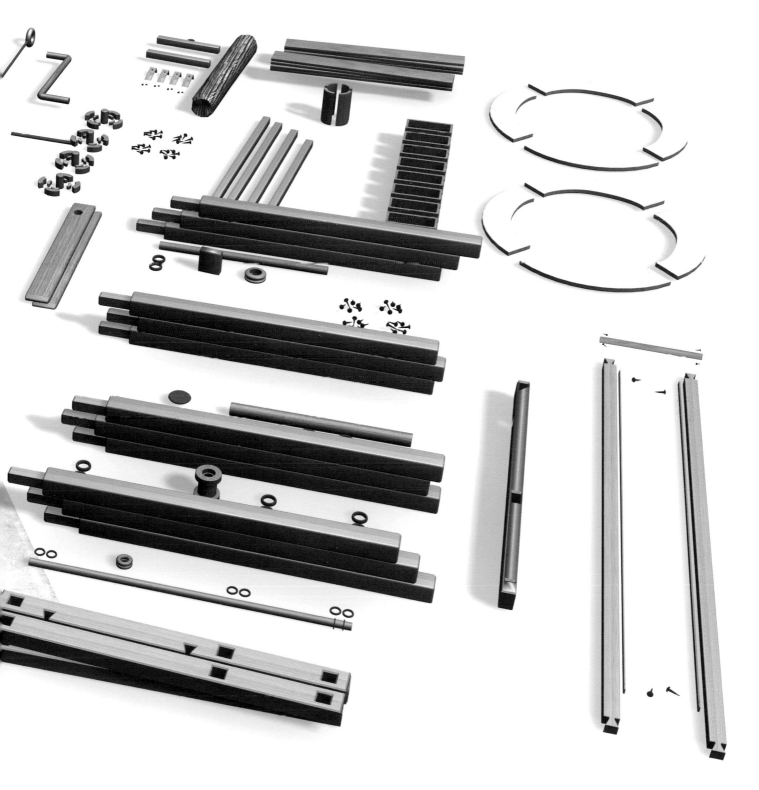

fig. 6
*The image shows the mechanical saw
disassembled and surrounded by its parts:
structural parts, gears, joints,
couplings and mounts.*

Vinci, 1452

1460

1470

1480

1487-1489

1490

1500

1510

Amboise, 1519

Codex Atlanticus, f. 945r

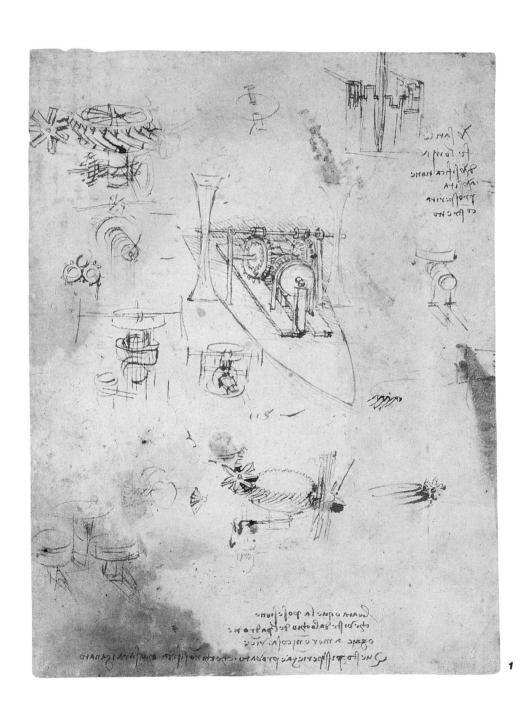

1

Paddleboat

Boats based on new systems of propulsion, underwater diving suits, submarines, mechanisms to attack enemy ships from the under the sea: Leonardo was often interested by research in the nautical field, and he often came up with highly original solutions. Sea and river (when possible) navigation was the fastest and most effective means of communication of the time. Cities such as Milan and Florence without any form of direct water connection to the sea lived this limitation with great difficulty, and given their political and economic power, they strived to overcome it. These efforts were directed both in the military field (Milan's expansionistic aims towards the Ligurian coast, or, the ever-continuing war declared by Florence against Pisa), as well as in the field of hydraulic engineering. Often these efforts were at the limits of the impossible, as with the Florentine attempt to render the Arno River navigable to the sea. The design for new types of vessels gets much attention by Renaissance engineers, especially with regards to ever-increasing commercial and wartime demands. The basic concept of a vessel moved by paddlewheels is a project that had already been amply dealt with by previous engineers, from Taccola to Francesco di Giorgio. Leonardo makes notable improvements to the paddle-moving mechanisms and offers a new way of approaching the problem. Almost every new invention or design modification for one or other of the mechanisms passes before our eyes in disordered but very effective visual notes. In the manuscripts by engineers contemporary to Leonardo the designs for paddleboats are generally presented in their final form, without an indication of the research process behind them. Leonardo has recently arrived in Milan when he makes drawings on this folio. There is a series of elements that suggest the period to be around 1487-1489. Among these are the Lombard names on the reverse of the folio in handwriting that is not Leonardo's. It is one of the many pages from the accounting ledger for the Milan Cathedral that ends up in Leonardo's possession, and he uses it for inserting drawings and notes in the blank spaces. The other element that would confirm the dating of this folio is the list of words in the upper right: 'Fellonia'. Diversificazione. Avversità [...]' (misdeed, diversification, adversity). The long lists of words in the manuscripts from this period (Manuscript B and Codex Trivulzianus) attest to the fact that once Leonardo reached Milan, not having had a regular university-level education and desirous of accessing the cultural sources of the era, he began the long exercise of learning linguistics, including Latin.

2

fig. 1
The folio 945r in the Codex Atlanticus. In the centre there is a pedal mechanism for propelling the boat, a very important technical device. Surrounding it are other construction details and various notes.

fig. 2
Rotating paddle device activated by the propulsion mechanism of the pedals. The navigation of rivers and canals poses different problems than sea navigation. Once the flotation problem was worked out, the vessel had to have a propulsion system allowing it to move upstream as well as to quickly move through the slow waters of the canals. The use of a paddlewheel seemed to Leonardo to be a better solution than the use of oars. The basic idea in this innovation was to substitute oars with wheels, using a working principle opposite to that used in mills: not the action of the water moving a wheel, but rather the manual action of the paddle on the wheel in the water making the vessel move.

fig. 3
*Exploded view of all the parts
of the reciprocating-motion motor.*

fig. 4
*Diagram of the workings of the pedal
motor on the paddleboat.
The mechanisms for the left block
are in transparency, while the right
block (its workings are explained)
is highlighted. It is interesting to note
the use of systems that transform
linear reciprocating motion into
uniform continuous rotary motion.
This mechanism is similar to one
of Leonardo's drawings on folio 30v
in the Codex Atlanticus, with some
of the parts inverted.*

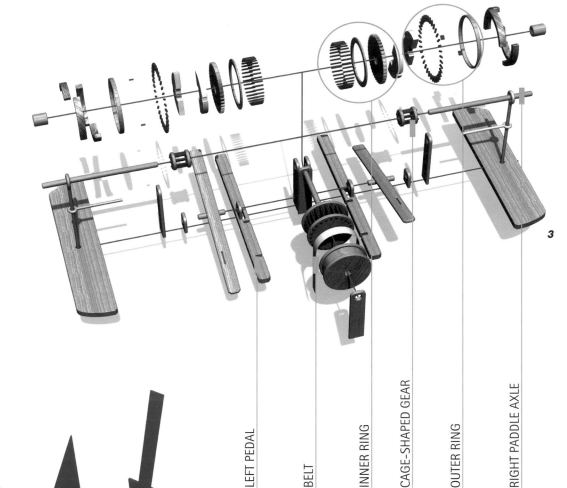

3

LEFT PEDAL

BELT

INNER RING

CAGE-SHAPED GEAR

OUTER RING

RIGHT PADDLE AXLE

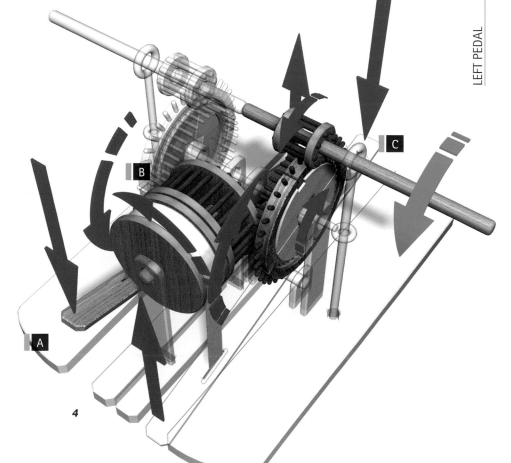

4

A One or more men on the boat begin by pushing the left pedal. This pulls a belt that makes the centre mechanism rotate.

B Worked by the belt, the centre mechanism rotates clockwise, transmitting its movement to the inner right ring on the motor block. Two inner springs turn clockwise engaging and meshing the outer toothed-ring.

C The outer ring transmits the rotary motion to the upper gear that begins to rotate in a counter-clockwise direction. The motion is then transmitted to the right support axle, moving the paddle-wheel that rotates counter-clockwise (green arrow). After this sequence, the right pedal is pushed and the process continues in alternation.

overleaf, following page,
fig. 7
*Rendering of a paddleboat (the one described in
folio 1063r in the Codex Atlanticus powered by
the arms) as it may have seemed to Leonardo
from the Torre del Falconiere in the Castello
Sforesco in Milan, viewed from the inner moat.*

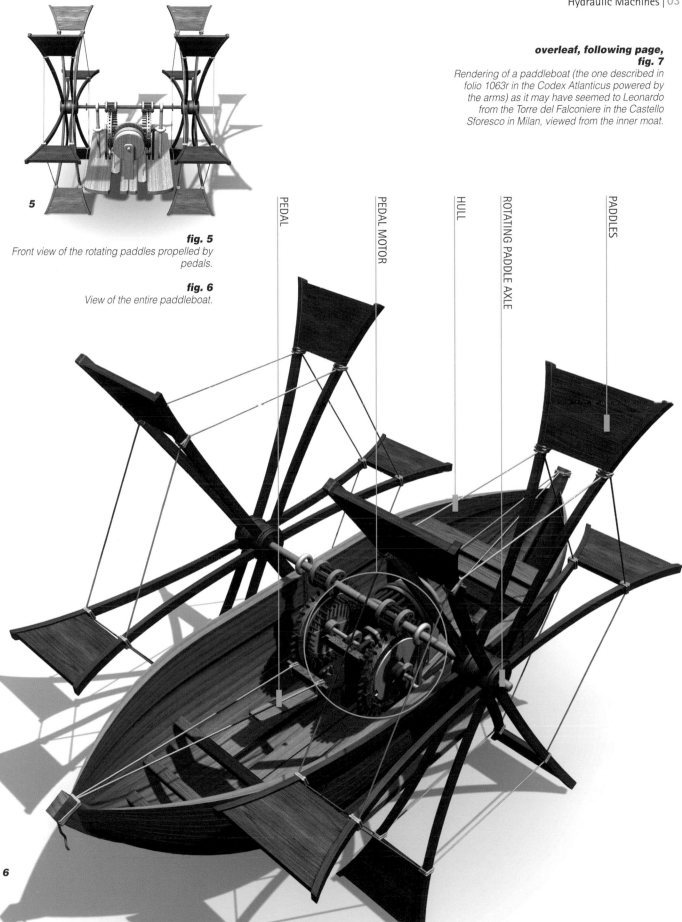

5

fig. 5
*Front view of the rotating paddles propelled by
pedals.*

fig. 6
View of the entire paddleboat.

PEDAL

PEDAL MOTOR

HULL

ROTATING PADDLE AXLE

PADDLES

6

Vinci, 1452

1460

1470

1480

1487-1489

1490

1500

1510

Amboise, 1519

Codex Atlanticus, f. 855r

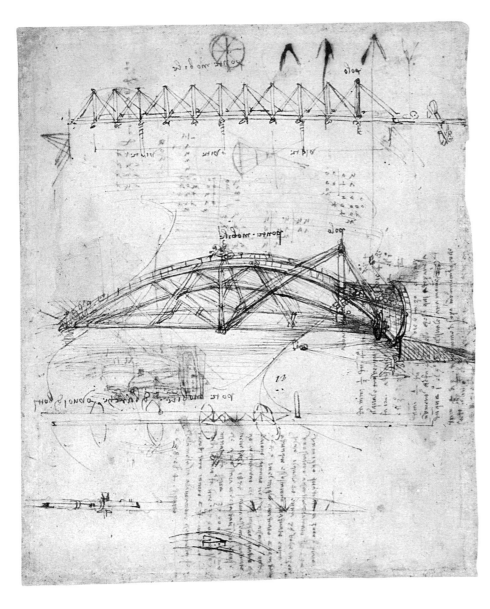

1

Swing Bridge

One of the most interesting chapters in Leonardo's work is the design of bridges to be used principally during wartime. In the letter of introduction he writes to Ludovico il Moro after having left Florence in 1482, he mentions he can build 'bridges that are extremely light-weight and strong'. We do not know if Ludovico il Moro put the young and ambitious Tuscan engineer to the test. Certainly, Leonardo's notes contain numerous drawings about how to construct bridges with characteristics that were particularly useful during wartime. Bridges that were mobile (the type of bridge reconstructed here), that were constructed with very light materials, that could be assembled and disassembled easily and rapidly. The testimony of Luca Pacioli, great mathematician and friend to Leonardo, is also very interesting. In his *De viribus quantitatibus* he speaks about a 'noble engineer' who, for Cesare Borgia the ill-famed 'Valentino', had invented emergency bridges for use in battle that could be easily assembled without the use of tools such as cords or metal. It is not certain that Pacioli is referring to Leonardo; but the reference may well have been to the Maestro in light of the fact that Leonardo worked for 'il Valentino' as a military engineer. The three studies on this page present three variations on bridges: a bridge constructed with poles (the type easily assembled and disassembled), a swing bridge and a floating bridge resting on boats or pontoons. They are quick sketches, ideas that Leonardo temporarily records to be refined at a later time. Manuscript B contains many sketches of this type, and in fact, the folio from the Codex Atlanticus here almost surely dates from the same period, the years just after Leonardo's arrival in Milan.

As often is the case for wartime devices Leonardo draws in part from tradition. His floating bridge on boats has almost a classical sense about it. This is not a sign of a defect in originality: during this period Leonardo is trying to make headway in the Milanese court, and as for other warrior-princes of the time, the needs and abilities in the art of war even for 'il Moro' are fused with the humanistic tendency to give this activity a dimension of re-born classicism. Putting hints of structures and ideas having classical origins in with his innovative designs would have played in Leonardo's favour. Even so, the originality in these projects, especially in the moveable bridge, is prevalent. Leonardo's notions related to statics are particularly remarkable. He uses the term 'pole' for the vertical pivot around which the bridge rotates, and other contrivances (the caisson acting as a counterweight) evoke this theoretical horizon. The science 'de ponderibus', the study of the static and dynamic behaviour of bodies, is one of the first theoretical areas broached by Leonardo when he arrives in Milan. His contribution to this field is applying science, traditionally confined to purely theoretical speculation, to a context of practical mechanics.

fig. 1
Folio 855r in the Codex Atlanticus. The three studies on this sheet present three variations of bridges: a bridge constructed with poles (the type easily assembled and disassembled), a swing bridge and a floating bridge resting on boats or pontoons.

fig. 2
Overhead view of the swing bridge.

2

The drawing of this bridge dates from Leonardo's first period in Milan, and like the others probably is part of those projects he mentions in the letter to 'il Moro' where he commends his capabilities in civil and military engineering. The main characteristic of this bridge is that it could be quickly closed and opened, making it an effective tool in halting the advancing enemy.

fig. 3
View of the swing bridge on the folio in which it appears, CA 855r in fig. 1 (previous page).

fig. 4
View of the swing bridge from below, showing some of the structural components and the respective functioning mechanisms.

SECONDARY RAMP

PAVEMENT

SUPPORT STRUCTURE

ARCHES

LOWER BASE

HANDRAIL

OPENING WINCH

CENTRAL PYLON

ACCESS RAMP

CLOSING WINCH

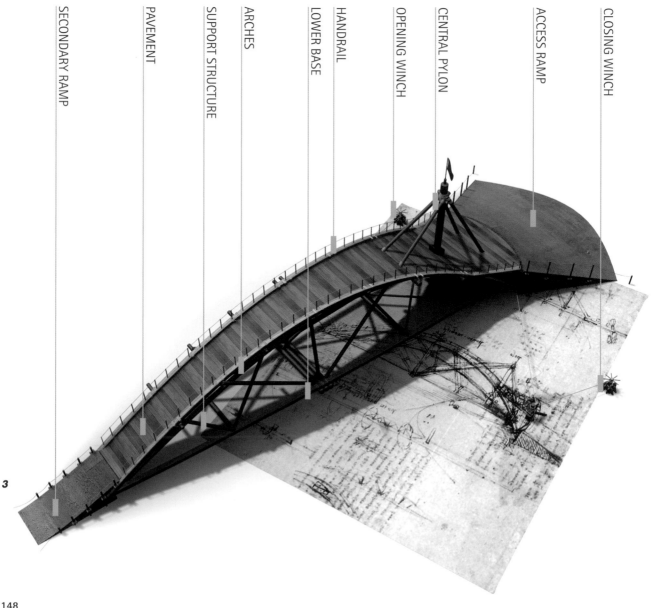

3

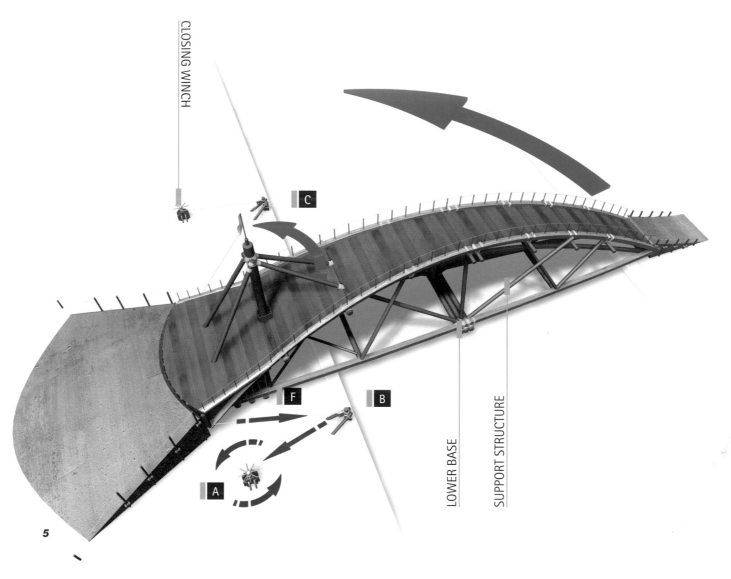

CLOSING WINCH

C

F

B

A

LOWER BASE

SUPPORT STRUCTURE

5

This bridge, constructed with only one span, is fixed to one of the banks by a verti-cal pivot that allows it to rotate. Using a system of cords, winches and rollers to facilitate movement, the bridge rotates so that vessels can pass, or so one side of the river can be isolated.

A Opening winch for the bridge: as it turns, the line connected to the bridge is wound in.

B A system of pulleys fixed to the bank keeps the line from slipping and determines the trajectory, optimising the rotation the swing bridge has to make in order to open.

C By pulling the lines, the bridge is made to rotate on the central pylon, and thus sus-pended, opens the way for vessels to pass through. The pylon functions as a pivot pin, like on a balance.

fig. 5
Functional diagram of the swing bridge while opening.

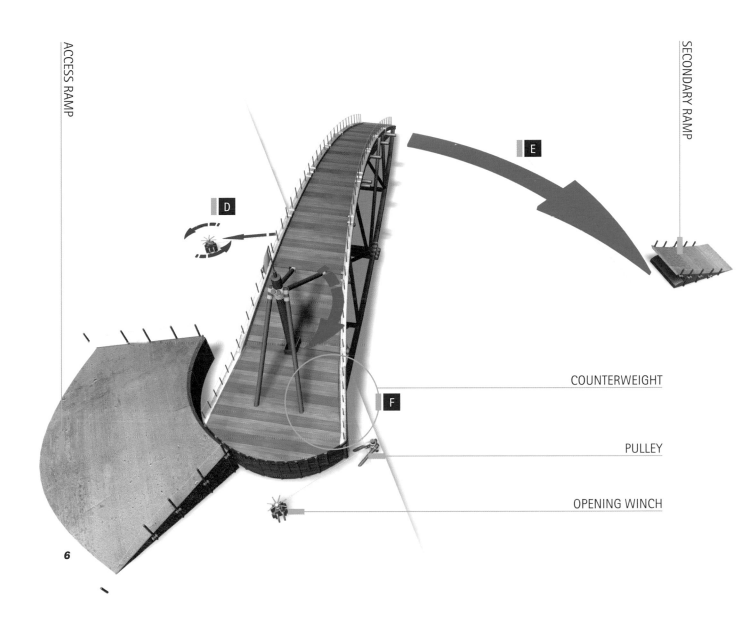

ACCESS RAMP

SECONDARY RAMP

D

E

COUNTERWEIGHT

PULLEY

OPENING WINCH

F

6

fig. 6
Functional diagram of the swing bridge while closing.

overleaf, following pages,
figs. 7 and 8
Hypothetical images of the swing bridge
installed on a river.
In the first, all the parts of the bridge seen in
transparency are disassembled and placed next to it.
The second shows the bridge closed, as it would have
appeared to Leonardo.

D In order to bring the bridge back to its initial position and allow for its crossing, the opposite winch, farthest from the pylon is activated. The line is wound in, pulling with it the end of the bridge.

E The end of the bridge is re-aligned with the secondary access ramp, placed on the opposite bank from the rotation pylon.

F To makes the opening of the bridge easier, Leonardo planned for a stone caisson to serve as a counterweight when the bridge is suspended and before it rests on the other bank

Vinci, 1452

1460

1470

1480

1490

1500

1510

1513-1514

Amboise, 1519

Manuscript E, f. 75v

1

Dredger

2

The study for this machine that dredges mud from the bottom of a canal is inserted in one of the manuscripts that Leonardo uses during the last years of his life. The manuscript is in a small format, and is comprised of ninety-six sheets, like two other codices from the same period, Manuscripts G and F. It obviously represents a size that Leonardo believed to have the optimal number of pages for a small volume and still not be too heavy and cumbersome to carry. He travelled frequently, and the ease in handling the instruments for his own thoughts was certainly important. Manuscript E contains a relevant biographical note about Leonardo's transfer from Milan to Rome in 1513. Can we thus deduce that the project for the dredger also dates to the years he spent in Rome? We can not be certain of this. The presence of a date in one of Leonardo's manuscripts does not exclude he may have previously begun some notations in that manuscript. What is certain is that while he is in Rome he is involved in an undertaking for which machines like the one drawn in Manuscript E would have been quite useful: the grandiose land reclamation project of the Pontine Marshes, the area south of Rome between Sermoneta and Terracina, close to the Tyrrhenian Sea. In 1514, Pope Leo X gives his brother Giuliano de' Medici the task of initiating the land reclamation work. A document mentions the 'highly skilled land-surveyors', that is to say, the group of engineers undertaking the project. Leonardo was also among these. Giuliano de' Medici, powerful brother of the Florentine pontiff, was Leonardo's patron in Rome. Also, among the folios by Leonardo kept in the British Royal collections there is a magnificent drawing (Windsor RL 12684) giving an aerial view of the entire Pontine flatlands around Mount Circeo, the land reclamation area. Leonardo even indicated the work that had to be done: clean the mud from Rio Martino that periodically continued to overflow, and in general, carry out a series of works that would contain this and other waterways by digging ditches and channels. Could it be that the dredging machine was part of these projects? Even while in Milan during the years immediately preceding this period, Leonardo worked for the French on the containment of waterways. Thus, it is certainly possible that the studies for the dredging machine, if not made during the Roman undertaking, where useful in Milan.

After making the drawing, adding the title (top) and the main notes below, due to the limited space and in order to add further observations, Leonardo was forced to use smaller calligraphy, squeezing in a long note along the lower margin and another in the right margin.

fig. 1
Folio 75v from Manuscript E.
The upper portion of the page shows a carefully drawn dredger in action.
Below, an articulate series of notes describes its structure and workings.

fig. 2
Overhead view of the dredger. The double-hull boat structure can be clearly seen. It stabilises the flotation, similar to the modern-day catamaran.

3

4

fig. 3
Diagram of the workings of the dredger.

fig. 4
Scoop wheel on the dredger.

fig. 5
View of the dredger as it dredges a riverbed, in a section diagram to show the riverbed.

fig. 6
Overall view of the dredger in action.

A The dredging machine is comprised of two boats parallel to one another with a large, scoop wheel in the centre that empties the material dug up from the river bed onto a barge.

B Leonardo designed a turn-crank mounted directly onto the axle of the scoop wheel that winds a cord around the hub. Because the cord is still anchored to the shore, the dredger automatically advances and the work progresses.

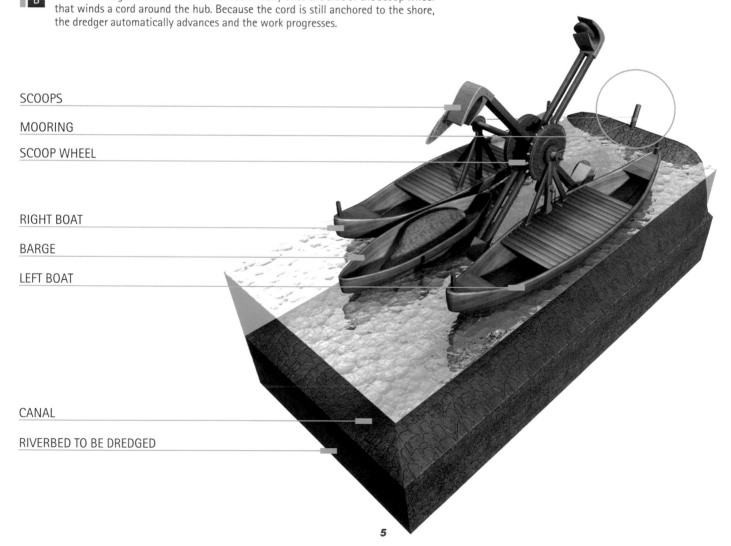

SCOOPS

MOORING

SCOOP WHEEL

RIGHT BOAT

BARGE

LEFT BOAT

CANAL

RIVERBED TO BE DREDGED

5

004 **Work Machines**

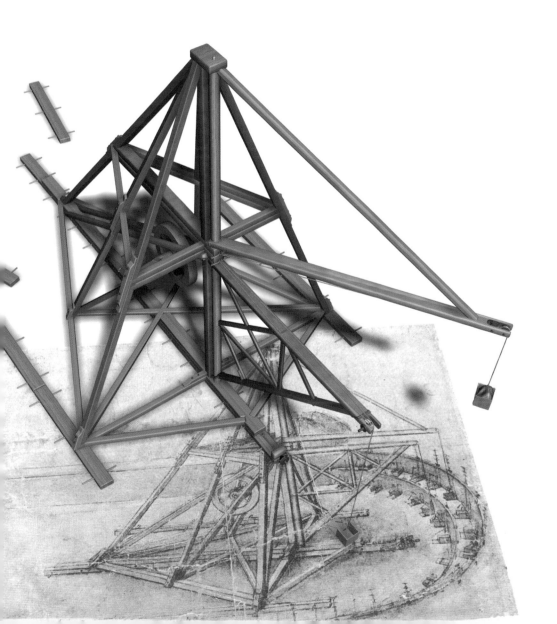

Metallurgy, hoists for lifting and placing materials on construction sites, machines for the textile industry: all different types of mechanical projects aimed at optimising work efficiency that Leonardo worked on throughout his life. As in other areas of his work, before he could innovate he had to understand. During the late 1400s in Florence, Leonardo came into contact with two great schools of technical learning: Verrocchio's workshop where he was apprenticed, and the Brunelleschi worksite for the construction of the dome on the cathedral. Leonardo reveals the importance of Verrocchio's lessons in a late notation. On 27 May 1472, to the stupor of all present, Verrocchio completed Brunelleschi's great undertaking by placing an enormous copper-gilt ball on top of the dome. The casting of this sphere had been complex, and was carried out under the attentive eye of Leonardo. In fact, forty years later when faced with similar problems, Leonardo writes: 'Remember the how the ball on Santa Maria del Fiore was welded [...] in copper impressed in stone, like the triangles of this ball' (Ms. G, f. 84v). Verrocchio's workshop produced not only sublime bronze statues; utilitarian objects in metal such as bells or armour were also produced. When he entered the workshop as an apprentice painter, Leonardo found himself in a very versatile environment. It does not surprise us therefore, to find engineering designs by young Leonardo made for reverberatory furnaces and burning mirrors (for example, Codex Atlanticus, f. 87r). The empirical purpose of these studies is quite clear. The burning mirrors were used to fuse or weld metal by using reflection and the concentration of heat produced by reflection. Even the reverberatory furnaces were meant to indirectly fuse metals using reflected fire, creating heat reverberated from the walls. During this period, 'reflection' was a law that greatly interested Leonardo from another point of view as well. At the basis of optics and perspective was the complexity of optical and geometrical laws relative to the natural vision of space and objects, and their pictorial reproduction. It is most likely that Leonardo's theoretical knowledge of perspective influences the more theoretical studies linked to the empirical design of burning mirrors. For example, on folio 87r in the Codex Atlanticus he studies a grinding device, a machine meant to give the correct curvature to a mirror (by creating a parabolic curve, as in the section of a cone).

The machines used by Filippo Brunelleschi, crucial elements in the construction of the Florentine dome and in the success of the entire undertaking, encompass the other great school open to the young Leonardo. The invention of the new machines for the worksite along with innovative construction criteria made it possible to build the enormous architectural structure without the use of temporary framework.

Many of the projects in the Codex Atlanticus (for example, ff. 808r, 1083v, 965r, 138r) point out the young genius's interest in these devices.

Leonardo's most important projects for textile machinery date from his years in Milan. Generally, in both Florence and Milan, the primary goods (wool) were imported from Germany and Flanders. It was transformed on-site in essentially three phases: cleaning the fibre, spinning (stretching, twisting and winding onto a bobbin), weaving to obtain a piece of fabric. Dyeing was another fundamental passage. Machines were necessary for each of these phases. As seen in some of the studies in the Codex Madrid I (circa 1495) or in the Codex Atlanticus, Leonardo designed machines primarily used for spinning. Here again, before he begins innovating he studies what already exists. In fact, it may be that a very beautiful drawing in the Codex Madrid I (f. 68r) was not one of his inventions but a very careful study of a loom used in a Milanese spinning-mill. Other projects in the same manuscript are very ingenious studies that go beyond beautiful graphics, concentrating directly on the mechanical content of the drawing while attempting to optimise efficiency and speed of the device. For example, the project for a flyer spindle assembly in the Codex Atlanticus (f. 1090v) attempts to synchronise three different operations: stretching the fibres, twisting, and winding up the bobbin. After 1500, during his mature phase, Leonardo more than once revisits his studies on metallurgy, cranes, construction-site machines as well as textile machinery. Now, however, his projects are increasingly intellectual and sophisticated. Some projects for excavation machinery and hoists (Codex Atlanticus, ff. 3r and 4r) date almost certainly from the early 1500s. One of the machines operated by a treadwheel is slightly more traditional, and may have served as a point of comparison with a more innovative project where the problem of the driving force (lifting containers filled with earth from an excavation site) is solved by using weights and counterweights. The machine itself looks like an enormous set of scales, the materialisation of one of Leonardo's studies on the behaviour of weights, the science of 'de ponderibus' to which he dedicated himself with ever-increasing intensity. We are clearly beyond the empirical horizon of Brunelleschi's machines: in this machine, theoretical knowledge and the solution of concrete problems are integrally combined. A few years later in Rome, around 1513-1516, Leonardo's interest in metallurgy and textile machinery emerges in a new form. Manuscript G contains a series of notes on the construction of burning mirrors. More explicitly and systematically than during his youth in Florence, this area of study is now enriched with theoretical content. Leonardo undertakes complex research on reflection (for example, Codex Atlanticus, f. 750r), and in order to define the parabolic shape of the mirror with precision, Leonardo develops a complicated compass. While at the Vatican, Leonardo must remain on close watch for unethical competition from a technician, a certain Giovanni degli Specchi (John 'of the mirrors'), who like Leonardo works for Giuliano de' Medici, brother of Pope Leo X. At one point in some of his notes on burning mirrors, Leonardo inserts ciphered words to make his projects less comprehensible. We do not know how knowledgeable Giovanni degli Specchi may have been. The fact that he was German is significant. Throughout the *Quattrocento* in Germany metallurgy underwent important developments correlated by the production of treatises. Only later in Italy were the works by the Sienese author Vannoccio Biringucci and of course Leonardo available to guide the innovations made to the scientific foundations in this field. Thus, to have an untrustworthy German technician buzzing about must have created a sizeable problem for Leonardo. In terms of the burning mirrors, it is possible that these were intended for the textile industry, which in Rome under the Medici pope, was in expansion. Nonetheless, it is interesting that at least in one case Leonardo envisioned a different destination for these studies: astronomy and the reflecting telescope (based on a note in the Codex Arundel, f. 279v). Leonardo mentions another cultural aspect of projects with mirrors when he cites how Archimedes used them against the Romans in the defence of Syracuse. Even the two projects for twisting twine into very thick cords (Codex Atlanticus, ff. 12r and 13r) hold cultural meaning. During this time Fra Giocondo dedicates the edition of the treatise with machine illustrations by Vitruvius, *De architectura,* to Giuliano de' Medici. Leonardo, in turn, dedicates his two projects to the Medici and most likely to Giuliano who was his patron and protector. On one of the two machines there is a handle in the shape of a ring set with a diamond: one of the most recognisable Medici symbols.

Vinci, 1452

1460

1470

1478-1480

1480

1490

1500

1510

Amboise, 1519

Codex Atlanticus, f. 30v

1

Reciprocating Motion Machine

It is probable that initially Leonardo drew only two projects on this page. The first was a hoist based on the transformation of the reciprocating motion of a lever into rotary motion necessary to lift a weight. The second was a strangely shaped ladder that in traditional terms had no conceptual connection to the former. The two inventions, however, are presented in finished versions, with hatching and ink wash, and thus make up part of the mechanical drawings used in presentations containing one, or at the most, two large-scale images (another example is found on folio 24r in the Codex Atlanticus). Francesco di Giorgio put together an album with analogous drawings. As in other cases, the well-finished presentation is a fleeting moment in his work and Leonardo inserts a backward-written note about the hoist (thus, a personal note). In the upper left corner he also sketches a study for an hygrometer, a system based on the use of a spongy substance (capable of water-absorption) on the left side of a balance, with a water-repellent substance (wax) placed on the opposite side. As the humidity in the air increases and water is absorbed, the scales tip further to the left, indicating a worsening in the weather conditions. Thus, before these additions, the folio was dominated by two magnificent drawings of machines, a traditional formula to which Leonardo adds his own radical innovations. These can be seen in the design for the hoist: it is fully drawn with all the mechanisms fitted into one another. On the right side of the sheet, Leonardo shows these same mechanisms split apart depicted in the same sense and order of their relationship to each other. This is one of the first and most effective examples of an exploded view, an iconographical means Leonardo will later systematically apply to other studies including his studies on human anatomy. The presence of an exploded view in one of his youthful drawings for a machine brings up the problem of cross-influence extending over various areas of his research. We have no anatomical drawings from this same period (although various elements induce us to believe they existed). Nevertheless, based on the drawing here we can deduce that machine design was at a reasonably mature level very early on, thus acting as a source of ideas for other fields: before human and animal anatomy, Leonardo drew the anatomy of machines. The relationship between the overall view and the exploded view is not the only type of revolutionary iconographical resource used in depicting this machine. To the right, the shaft and a detail of the wheel are rotated and enlarged, and three letters synthetically suggest the main assemblage points between the various elements of the machine in their exploded view. Leonardo's visual language renders any additional text superfluous.

fig. 1
This folio contains one of the clearest and most explicit drawings by Leonardo. The full view of the machine is to the left, while the right side of the sheet shows an exploded view of the complex mechanism.

fig. 2
The reciprocating motion machine was an object of study. Based on the structure drawn on the folio, the device would have been able to lift considerable weight.

**overleaf, following page,
fig. 3**
Working diagram of the machine.

fig. 4
An exploded view of the reciprocating motion machine, very similar to the one designed by Leonardo.

2

A

Essentially, the reciprocating motion machine was meant as a study tool: Leonardo wanted to find a way to transform reciprocating motion produced by an operator into continuous rotary motion. In this project the operator worked the lever moving it from right to left; each time the lever moved, the two large mechanical wheels rotated slightly in opposite directions, first one and then the other, but never simultaneously.

B

The two large mechanical wheels hide a complex system of concentric mechanisms enclosed in two circular housings. The internal gears are made up of a wheel similar to a large saw with a mono-directional profile and a mechanism attached to the lever consisting of an internal circumference and two metallic spring pawls. Each time the lever moves the internal teeth alternately engage the two large external wheels that transmit motion to the central axle. A rhythmical clicking noise is produced.

C

The opposite circular movements of the two large mechanical wheels engage a cage-shaped gear wheel mounted on-axis with the main shaft. This gear wheel turns only in one direction, alternatively driven by both wheels. A line wound around the main shaft lifts the weight. Presumably, this project could have been used in civil mechanics, for example, in constructing a large-scale crane. A modern example of this machine is the mechanical jack.

3

TURNING AXLE SHAFT

LINE

LEVER

GEAR

FRAME

HOUSING

TOOTHED WHEEL

PEGS

WEIGHT

PAWL

4

Vinci, 1452

1460

1470

circa 1480

1490

1500

1510

Amboise, 1519

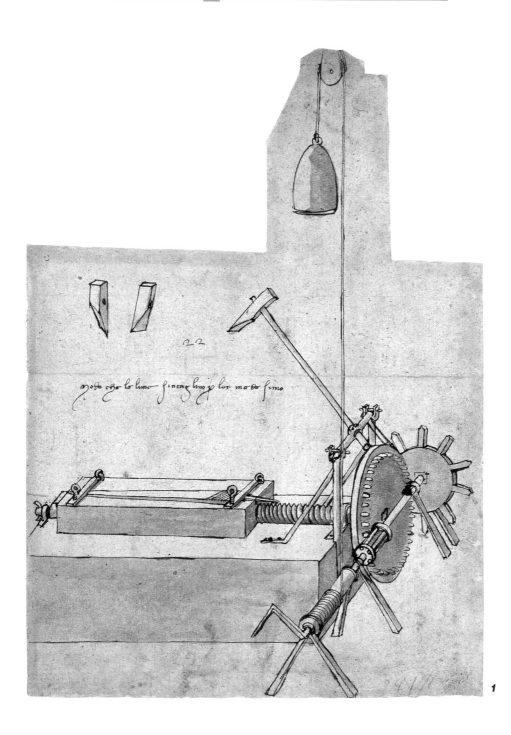

1

File-cutter

This folio contains a large, single drawing of a machine. The style of the drawing is well-finished with ample use of pen and ink and ink wash (a preparatory study is found on folio 1022v in the Codex Atlanticus). This page provides a perfect example of one of the ways Leonardo presented the drawings of his machines during the early years of his career. Although innovative in some aspects, the different ways Leonardo uses to make presentation drawings are rooted in the great tradition of mechanical drawing. In young Leonardo, as for the Sienese engineer Francesco di Giorgio, there are four principle forms to mechanical iconography: the private annotation (in form of a sketch); the placement of a single machine on the sheet executed in a very finished style; the composition on a single sheet of many highly-finished drawings of various machines (a sort of anthology in images); the integration of this combination with textual notes. Leonardo's drawing of a file-cutter is part of this second category of mechanical presentations. The *Opusculum de architectura*, written by Francesco di Giorgio and dedicated to the Duke of Urbino, Federico da Montefeltro, consists in a series of pages each with a very refined drawing of a single mechanical project. It is possible that Leonardo's drawing was also conceived with a similar-type album in mind. Its use for presentation is confirmed by the fact that his handwriting for the caption goes from left to right ('Modo che le lime s'intaglino per lor medesimo'; Way to cut files); a simple title added to a page where the visual language of the drawing was intended to dominate and to 'do the talking'.

The perspective used to depict the machine plays a fundamental role in the presentation of the image. The single viewpoint from the upper right, permits a complete view of the machine, both in its form and the relationship of its parts. The use of perspective in mechanical iconography not only improved communication but also had significant cultural meaning. Just as in painting, machines benefited from the scientific value they acquired with the application of the laws of perspective, natural geometry and mathematics. This is one of the main advances introduced by engineers, artists and authors like Francesco di Giorgio. Prior to this time, a machine was depicted based on iconographical conventions. Francesco di Giorgio was the first to radically change the way machines were depicted by using perspective, thus clearly representing the reciprocal relationship between the various elements in the machine. As shown by his drawing of the file-cutter, even Leonardo moves in this direction, taking the process of culturally emancipated drawing to its zenith.

fig. 1
Leonardo's drawing is very clear and shows how the machine functioned and was used.

fig. 2
The height of the pulley was an important consideration in the correct functioning of the entire device.

2

A In order to work, the machine had to be wound up; an operator turned the crank thereby hoisting a weight attached to a line and pulley positioned above the machine. The height of the pulley ensured that it would continue to function for a period of time; the higher the pulley the more the machine was wound, thus functioning for a longer period of time. Presumably, an operator was not required except for winding the mechanism. In fact, once the machine was functioning it cut the files in a completely automatic fashion.

B As in many of his projects, Leonardo tried to automate production processes and relieve the burden on man. The purpose of this machine is to produce files. A piece of pre-cut iron is positioned and fixed with screw clamps to the moving bed; the bed slowly slides along the top of the machine engaged by a long, sturdy worm screw.

C A large worm screw turned slowly, and engaging with the threads in the bed, it gradually moved towards the right side of the machine.

D A heavy hammer fell at regular intervals and every time it struck the piece of metal on the bed it left a sharp incision. When the whole length of the iron piece was incised, the file was ready to use.

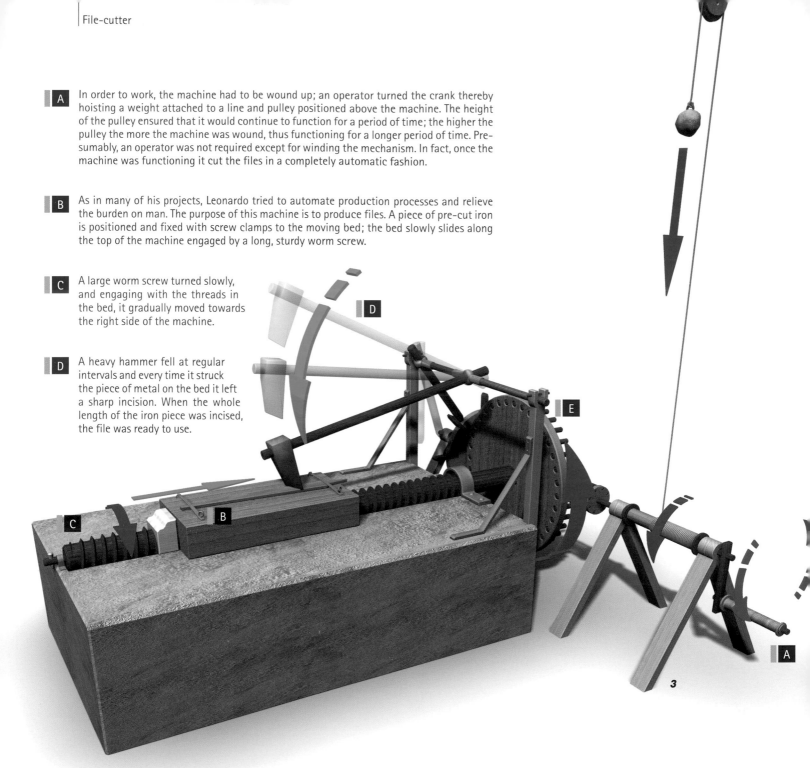

E The hammer falling on the file was regulated by a complex escapement system similar to the one used in watch making, but with must larger dimensions. A wheel periodically raised the handle of the hammer, but the same wheel once it finished its gear cycle let the hammer drop by gravitational force. The hammer was heavy and it struck the file with the required force to make the incision.

fig. 3
The diagram of the workings of the machine.

fig. 4
The main parts.

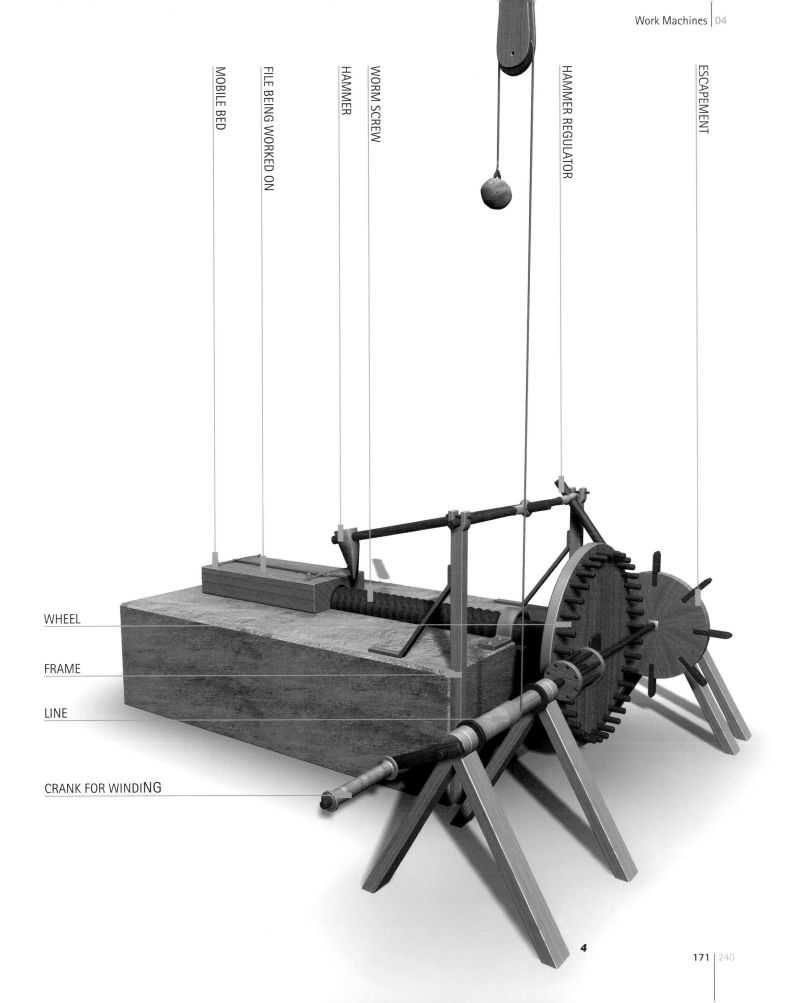

MOBILE BED

FILE BEING WORKED ON

HAMMER

WORM SCREW

HAMMER REGULATOR

ESCAPEMENT

WHEEL

FRAME

LINE

CRANK FOR WINDING

4

Vinci, 1452

1460

1470

circa 1480

1490

1500

1510

Amboise, 1519

Codex Atlanticus, f. 87r

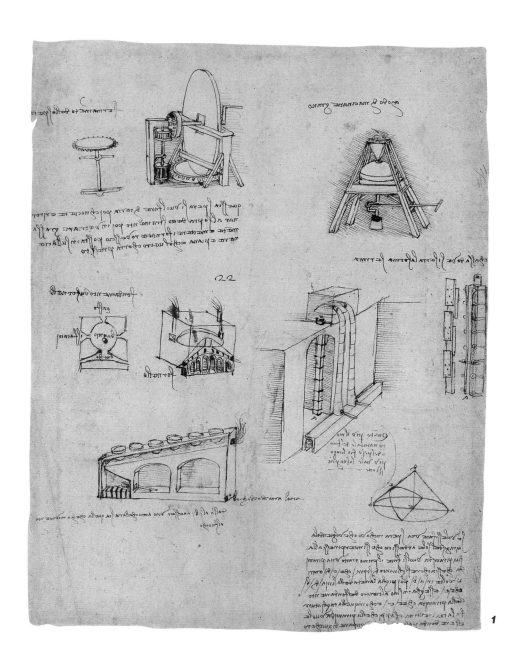

1

Device for Grinding Concave Mirrors

This page is typical of Leonardo's early years in Florence, where, in finished version and almost as an anthology of projects, he brings together various drawings. On this one page we find a grinding device used to make burning mirrors, a gristmill, and some ovens and burners. The dissimilar nature of the projects reveals their early, immature character. It is only later that Leonardo gives more theoretical rigour to his mechanical projects, but for the moment he confronts every problem as a separate case, following an empirical scheme typical of the workshops of the time. Still, there are a few very interesting traces that seem to steer Leonardo's thoughts towards the theoretical emancipation in mechanical design that will be fully realised years later. The project in the upper left of the page deals with producing burning mirrors, used throughout Florentine workshops of the period. Verrocchio's workshop, where Leonardo did his apprenticeship, made and positioned the enormous copper sphere for the dome of the cathedral of Santa Maria del Fiore. The sections of that sphere were welded together using a burning mirror. Leonardo himself recalls this memorable undertaking in 1472. Now old and famous, he makes a notation in Manuscript G referring to this experience when he returns to his studies on burning mirrors. The machine on this page certainly contains novel elements with respect to what was used in workshops such as Verrocchio's. Nonetheless, even more surprising is the study on the lower right of the same page: a diagram indicating how Leonardo intends to geometrically define the curvature of the mirror, a parabolic curve. Leonardo knows that paraboloids reflect the suns rays by concentrating them in a point called focus. Focus is also a term used in perspective, the science based on optics, which for the artists of the *Quattrocento* was the principle tool in theoretical elaboration. Thus it is understandable that Leonardo tried to apply the geometrical certainty of optics and perspective to the construction of burning mirrors. A diagram on folio 1055r in the Codex Atlanticus seems to be a study in optics. In reality, it is a careful attempt to geometrically define the curvature of the burning mirror. These are only minimal attempts, brief out-of-bounds moments, but nonetheless meaningful given later developments. On the page with the project for burning mirrors and its relative geometrical diagram, there is a project for a reverberatory oven that fires using reflected heat. Again, another example of theoretical overlapping between an area already recognised as science (perspective and optics for painters) and mechanical design, a field just beginning its journey towards that recognition.

fig. 1
In the upper part of the page there is a clear drawing of an automatic grinder for making mirrors; there are also a few handwritten notes.

fig. 2
The machine was used to make concave mirrors.

overleaf, following page, fig. 3
An image of the way the space around the machine may have looked, with an area for the finished mirrors, but also with heavy pieces of unworked stone.

fig. 4
The main parts of the machine.

A

When a man moved the lever, the various moveable parts of the machine were put in motion completing their circular trajectories. But before working the grinder, the operator had to position a stone to be cut under the large mill stone; the work involved to produce the concave stones must have been very tiresome due to the considerable weight that had to be moved. Once the lever was ready to be activated, the resistance and friction between grinding wheel and the mirror being worked must have been considerable.

The interesting part of this grinder is the combined rotation of the grinding wheel and the stone; the rubbing of these parts, evenly and uniformly smoothed the stone placed on the ground. Using an ingenious system of cage-shaped gears one or more persons could make all these movements by simply turning the crank.

B

The grinder was a very heavy object. Presumably, given its resistance to movement, all the moving parts had to be lubricated. The grinding wheel, activated by the crank on the side of the structure turned very slowly. Because it was very large, however, the angular velocity of its perimeter guaranteed sufficient friction speed without having to turn the handle too quickly. The stone placed under the grinding wheel turned in a perpendicular direction, incrementing the friction speed between the parts.

C

Smoothing and polishing presumably could have lasted even for a few days. Once one job was finished the machine was ready for another smoothing. Most likely, Leonardo even thought of a system to change the stone using a toothed wheel housing, and once the stone was in placed inside, it was positioned on the ground under the grinding wheel. Wedges, shown on the page, kept the pivot pin solidly in the ground.

STRUCTURAL REINFORCEMENTS

FRAME

GRINDING WHEEL

TRANSMISSION

GEARS

STONE

CRANK

Vinci, 1452

1460

1470

1480

1490

1500

1503-1504

1510

Amboise, 1519

Codex Atlanticus, f. 4r

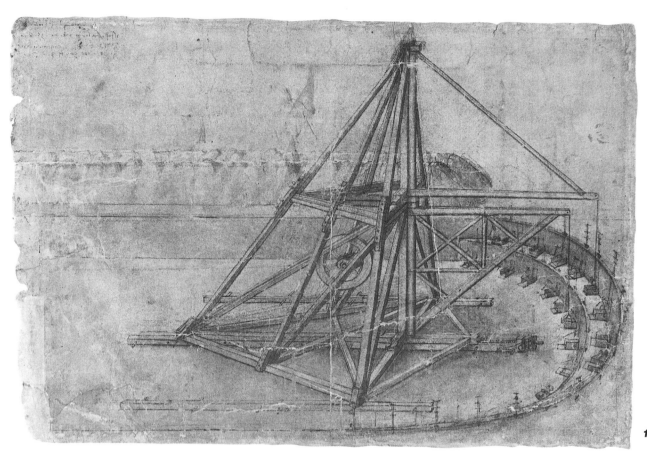

1

2

Canal Excavating Crane

This study, together with the analogous companion folio 3r in the Codex Atlanticus, is probably a demonstration model for a client. We know this because of its well-finished state. Leonardo first drew the general lines of the project in black pencil (traces of this first sketch can still be seen), then delineated the final drawing in pen and ink, and finished with an ink wash. It is therefore a study that was not just jotted down, but a highly finished rendering. It was a common practice for engineers, sculptors and architects to create models before constructing a final work. By observing the model, the client could request changes, or accept a proposal and consent to undertaking the work. The designer could either create three-dimensional scale models, or make drawings, almost always finished in ink wash, accurate in the details and overall form. Some of the models Michelangelo used for Julius II's funerary monument or for other architectural projects were very similar in style. It is probable that in using ink wash rather than his preferred technique of hatched rendering, Leonardo wanted to conform to the style usually used in presenting a drawing to a client. If the date of 1504 given to this folio is correct then the clients were probably representatives of the Florentine Republic. They had asked Leonardo to render the Arno River navigable, and thus this drawing would depict an excavating machine for a canal in the north of Florence, by-passing a section of the river that could not be navigated. In his youth, Leonardo had made analogous, highly refined drawings of machines set in the spatial context where they would function. A characteristic of this drawing is the complete lack of any human presence, devoid of the agile figures that in earlier drawings transformed the presentation of a machine into a lively and animated scene. Leonardo portrays an empty worksite, thereby emphasising the intellectual character of this study: the machine has a very calibrated, geometric form and proceeds on two, very regular, curved levels of excavation. The cases are all evenly spaced and the excavation tools (some suspended in the air) give an exact idea of the number of workers required. We do not know if Leonardo did, indeed, present these projects to prospective clients, or what their reaction may have been. This drawing, along with its pendant remained with the *maestro*, who at a certain point inserted a notation on the page using his normal backward handwriting; thus, a personal note regarding the two projects. Other less-finished drawings for cranes from the same period are found on folios 905 and 944v in the Codex Atlanticus and on folio 96r in the Codex Madrid I.

fig. 1
Folio 4r from the Codex Atlanticus.

fig. 2
A digital reconstruction of folios 3r and 4r from the Codex Atlanticus. Some of the marks on the drawing lead to the supposition that the two pages were originally one; especially at the embankments of the excavation site where there is a perfect fit at the point where they could be joined together.

overleaf, following pages,
fig. 3
Reconstruction of a hypothetical study model placed on the folio; it is very similar and surprisingly congruent with the 3D computer-generated view.

figs. 4 and 5
Diagrams for the workings of the crane.

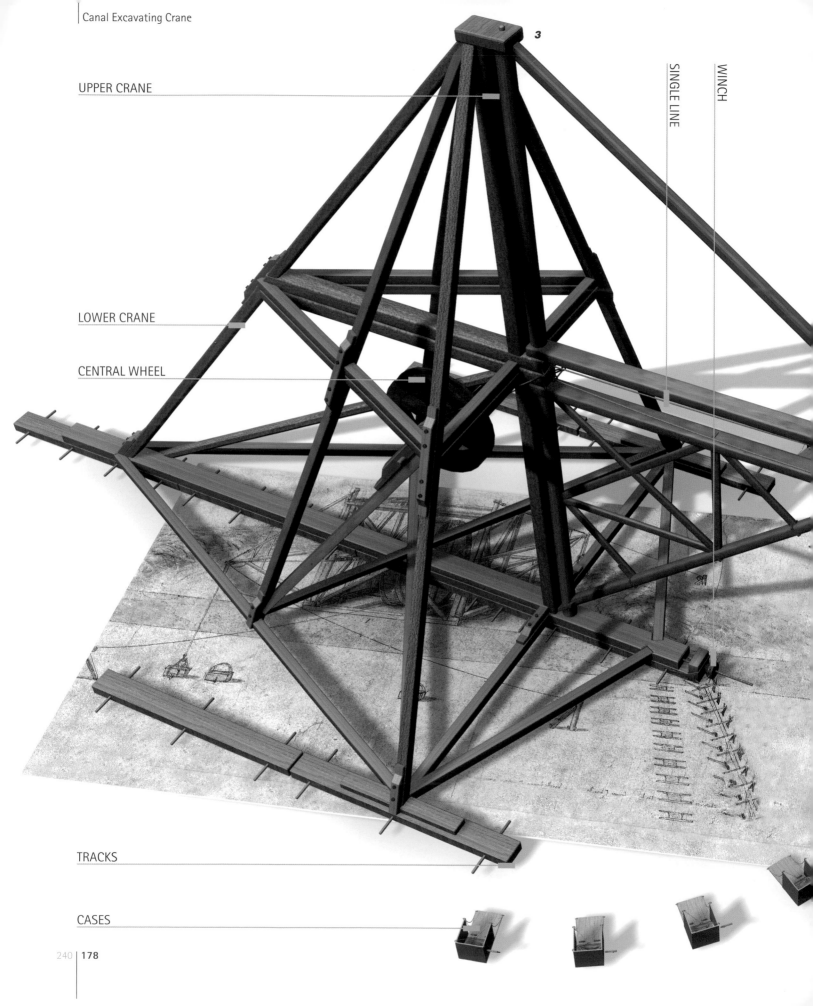

UPPER CRANE

SINGLE LINE

WINCH

3

LOWER CRANE

CENTRAL WHEEL

TRACKS

CASES

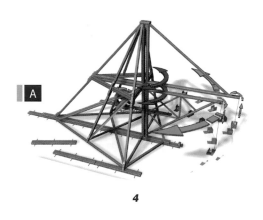

A Leonardo designed this machine to speed-up the time required to remove earth during the excavations for canals. Through an ingenious system of tracks and screws, the structure can be moved as the work advances. The machine consists in an enormous double-armed crane worked by a single cord and operating on the principle of a dumbwaiter. The teams of diggers work on three levels, synchronising their operations so that each time a container is full with earth, it is hoisted up, sending down the empty container with the diggers using it as a lift to return to their work stations.

4

B The work was organised as follows: while one team of diggers filled the cases on the bottom, another team emptied the case tied to the other end of the cord outside the canal itself. When the lower case was filled, the team on the outside – after having recuperated their energies – climbed inside the empty case returning to their work stations while the diggers on the bottom came up from the canal to empty the case filled with earth.

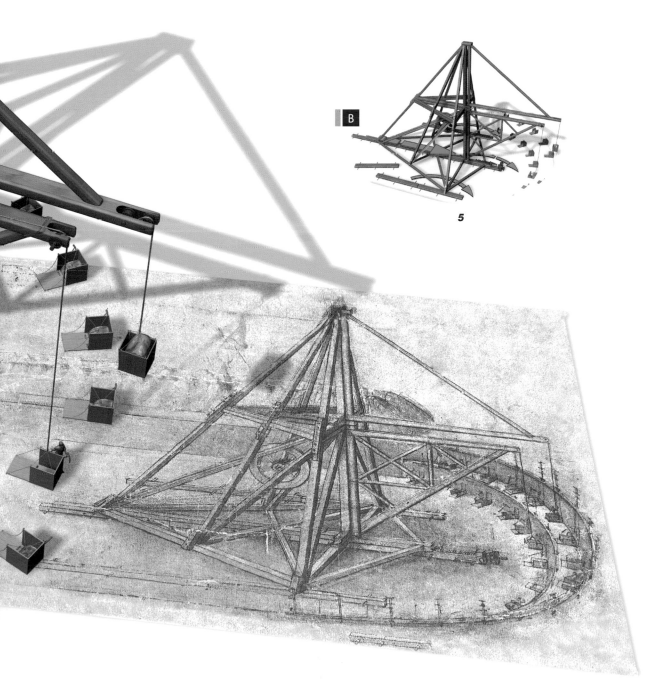

5

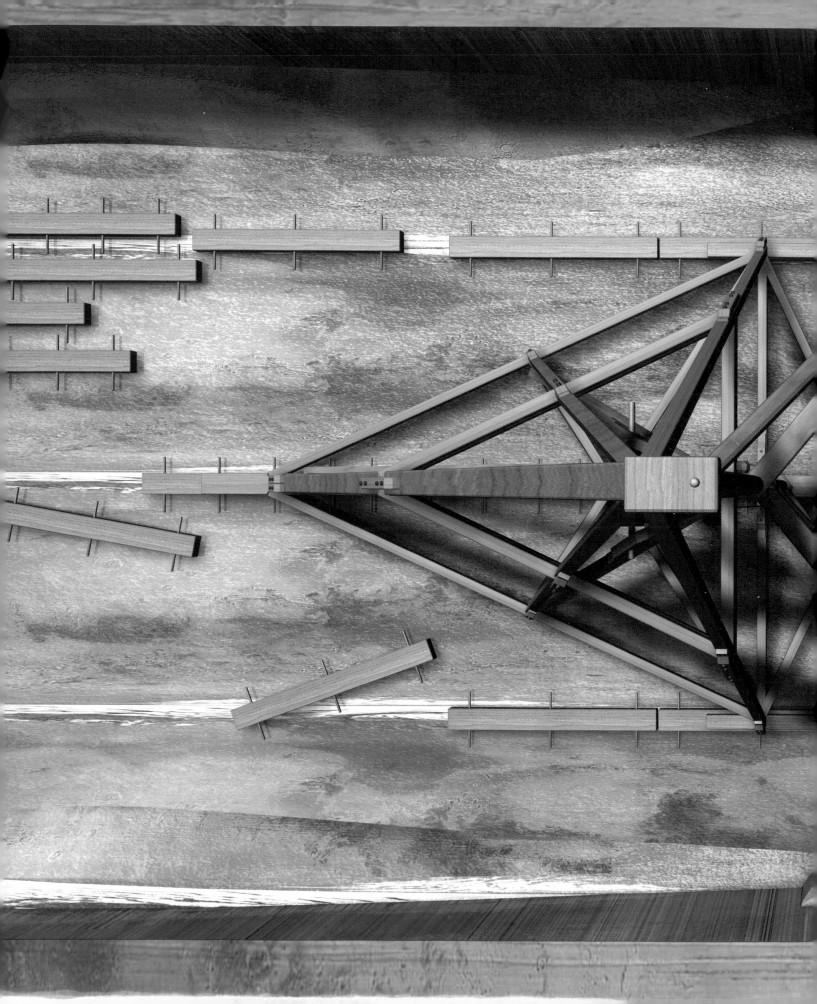

Self-propelled Cart
Theatrical Staging for *Orpheus*

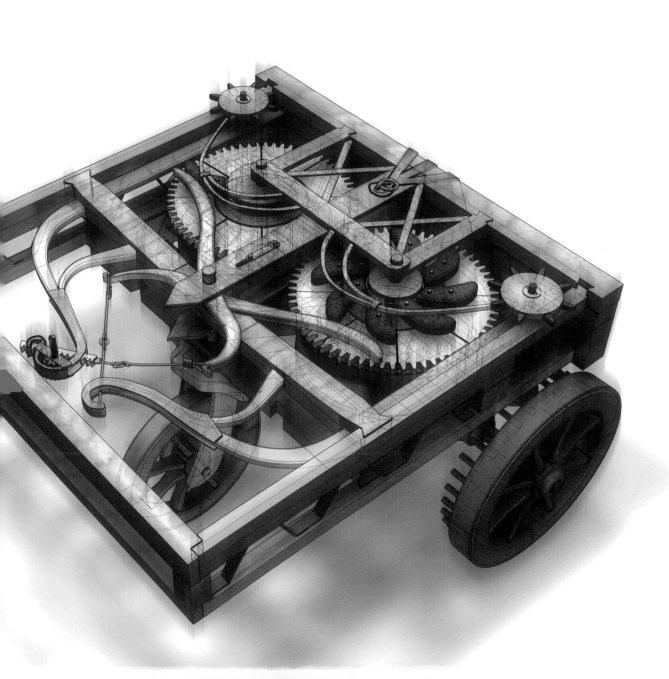

Many of the most important engineers and artists of the *Quattrocento* were often involved in making machines and stage settings for the theatre; engineers such as Giovanni Fontana and Brunelleschi, and artists ranging from Mantegna to Raphael. Leonardo is no exception. He designed theatrical devices and machinery even before leaving Florence; his abilities in this area were used in Milan for the Sforza, as well as later in his life at the court of France. Theatre during the Renaissance played upon the visual potential of dramatic productions, explaining the direct involvement of great artists and engineers. The set became a living painting in which actors, artists and machinators were all united in the same goal: to create a mimetic representation of reality, of an event. Normally, artists depicted reality through painting or sculpture. Theatre offered the chance to create paintings or sculpture that imitated reality not only in form but also in movement. For this purpose, automatons were often used, not just in the theatre but also as part of festivals. In addition to the very popular sacred plays and pageants of the Middle Ages, secular theatre became well established. Previously, this type of theatre was limited, having a generally low level of culture. Now, however, it becomes the most diffused form of theatrical representation especially among the more eminent levels of society.

It is not unusual, therefore, that all the great stage settings that Leonardo worked on were classical and secular in character (ranging from *Danaë* to the *Feast of Paradise* to *Orpheus*). Only during Leonardo's younger years in Florence do we find traces of interest in stage events that could involve sacred plays. On the other hand, these types of religious productions do not come to an end with the emergence of secular theatre. In Florence, sacred plays and pageants continue to grow in popularity and fortune. We know that in 1471 Verrocchio's workshop, where the young Leonardo was apprenticed, was given the commission for the stage settings and scenery for some of the sacred plays performed for Galeazzo Maria Sforza during his visit in Florence. As we can well imagine, these sacred themes are the perfect environment to stimulate the inventiveness and imagination of the machinators. In fact, Verrocchio was asked to stage scenes where structural elements or actors where capable of special movements, such as ascending and descending. With these factors in mind, it is not unusual that most certainly the first flying machine designed by Leonardo was for a stage set: diabolical machines with webbed wings that simulated flight on cable supports.

In the tradition of Florentine machinators, the importance given to movements of the scenery and sets will be fundamental for later developments in the Da Vincian concept of theatre. Just as in expressing other aspects of his creativity, in this area Leonardo progresses from a static and harmonious concept to one that is more dynamic and naturalistic. In order to understand this development, it is important to mention another innovation introduced in theatre during the Italian Renaissance. In the sacred plays of the Middle Ages, while one scene was going on various scenes set in different environments would appear, the 'side scenes': Pilate's palace, the garden of Gethsemani and so forth. The action in the various environments on stage infringed the Aristotelean principle of unity of action and space. In Renaissance theatre these visually fragmentary spectacles are offset by a unified scene, conceived and based on the criteria of perspective. The 'perspective setting' or 'urban scene' was developed by authors such as Baldassarre Peruzzi and Sebastiano Serlio following the precepts of the great classical architect Vitruvius. The comic or tragic action of the dramatisation was staged in an urban environment, with houses, piazza, and palaces in perspective succession. Leonardo seems to reflect, and in a certain sense anticipate, this type of theatrical setting in a small drawing on folio 996v from the Codex Atlanticus. The perspective is the same that most likely characterised the scenery for the *Feast of Paradise*, a dramatic performance staged by Leonardo during the 1490s for the Sforza court. Leonardo had astonished the audience by depicting Paradise with a large hemispherical canopy where actors rotated, each representing a planet. In the best of Florentine tradition it was a dynamic structure that certainly must have favourably impressed the unaccustomed Milanese court with its out-of-the-ordinary motion. Nonetheless, based on the descriptions we can say that despite its dynamic motion the device was dominated by a strong sense of order and harmony in keeping with the nature of the subject matter: the Aristotelean concept of the movement of the circular spheres through the heavens.

The 'perspective stage setting' elaborated during the course of the Renaissance presented a very static environment, and like perspective itself was dominated by geometric order. Many years later, again in Milan dominated by the French who have driven out the Sforza, Leonardo creates a stage setting for the myth of Orpheus, and we are presented with just the opposite concept. Leonardo had returned to dealing with theatrical spectacles as attested to in a page of the Codex Madrid I (folio 110r). Here, he designed a theatre consisting of two semicircles that while rotating could be transformed into an amphitheatre; a mobile theatre that combined into one structure the two main forms of classical theatre: the semicircle of Greek origins, used for theatrical, musical, literary events, and the amphitheatre with its Roman origins destined for gladiatorial spectacles. It was not an original invention, but rather an attempt – if only philological – at reconstructing Gaius Curio's hemispherical theatre, a mobile wooden structure described by Pliny the Elder in *Naturalis Historia*. In this context, Leonardo's interest in the dynamic aspect of theatre should be highlighted. There is a good number of drawings still extant related to the staging of *Orpheus* (Codex Arundel, ff. 231v, 264r; Codex Atlanticus, f. 363 and a folio once part of the Atlanticus, recently found in a private collection). It is clear from all these sketches that Leonardo's concept of a stage setting is the opposite of that held by the theoreticians of Renaissance 'perspective staging', at one time cherished by Leonardo himself. On one hand, Leonardo's setting is strongly naturalistic: there are no buildings, but rather a series of mountains and valleys. On the other hand, it is very dynamic in character: at a certain point, one of the mountains splits open and in ascending movement from the underworld the terrifying figure of Pluto (Hades) and other dreadful creatures emerge. Even if these quick sketches do not specifically depict wings, it is possible that these figures were winged, perhaps flapping wings like those designed during his youth in Florence. Thus, the development of Leonardo's conception of stage settings approaches the naturalistic and dynamic dimensions that are completely coherent with the other areas of his research during this same period (for example, the evolution of geometric perspective to aerial perspective).

During the last years of his life, Leonardo continues to work on inventions for pageants and stage events. For example, for a festival in Lyons put on by Florentine merchants in honour of the new king of France, Francis I, Leonardo designs an automaton: a lion, which after it advances, opens its chest spilling lilies onto the stage. Just as for his work machines from this period, even these '*ingegni*' for the theatre are packed with symbolism revolving around the complex games of political power: the lion is the symbol of Florence and at the same time refers to the French city of Lyons; the lilies are the symbol of the King of France. The message is clear, and the purpose is to thank Francis I, on the part of the Florentines and thus the Medici, for having descended into Italy and for reconquering Milan. Perhaps even some of the last, sublime drawings made by Leonardo in France are in reference to the theatre: on one side drawings of figures dressed in various attire, on the other, drawings for an equestrian monument (both conserved at Windsor Castle). The former are studies for theatrical costumes, the latter the design for an equestrian monument to be used as background set for a pageant or spectacle.

Vinci, 1452

1460

1470

1478-1480

1480

1490

1500

1510

Amboise, 1519

Codex Atlanticus, f. 812r

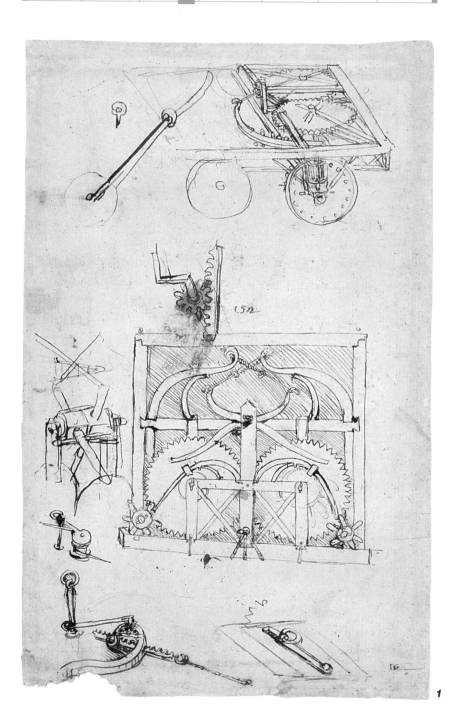

1

Self-propelled Cart

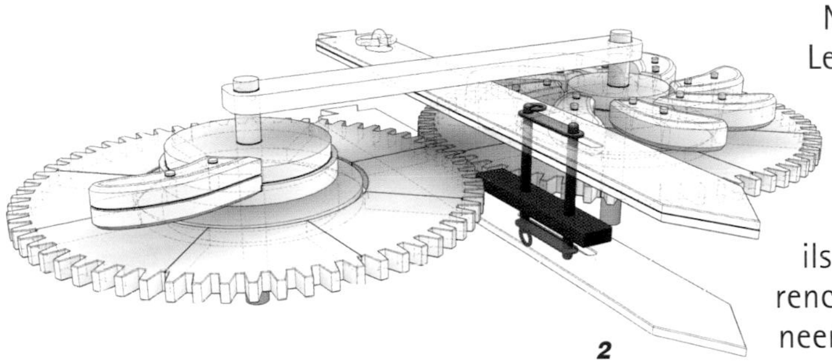

2

No more than a hypothesis, nonetheless, the use of Leonardo's famous 'auto-mobile' in a theatrical setting is a very interesting possibility. Even the first ideas for the flying machine are conceived in Florence during Leonardo's formative years. They appear in the margins of studies and projects for the mechanical wings of angels and devils destined for religious dramas, a very popular genre in Florence during the 1400s involving top-notch artists and engineers such as Filippo Brunelleschi. The folio is a typical working page, and just as in more finished drawings meant for public presentation, we perceive the importance that visual language transmitted through drawing had for Leonardo. The fact that not all the details are drawn or elaborated has often made it difficult for both past and present interpreters of this project. This is also due to the 'work-in-progress' nature of these drawings. Leonardo draws an idea and then he elaborates a few of the details involved with that phase. More so than with the presentation drawings, often ending up in either a whimsical or a heavily theoretical dimension, here we feel the concrete presence of a workshop. In fact, these drawings seem to be conceived as clarifications – for himself or others – on how to put together various parts of the mechanism. Leonardo worked on locomotive systems in other contexts as well. Wartime machinery was certainly an area where Leonardo, rapidly and often, had to solve problems such as those posed by the transport of heavy cannons. In this field he introduces various innovations related, for example, to the wheel sections or their alignment. He then studies locomotive systems themselves, and one of the devices most frequently employed is the three-wheeled cart. In an early drawing (Codex Atlanticus, f. 17v) he contrives an interesting system of auto-locomotion worked by one or two men placed inside the cart and an intelligent system of dynamic transformation and multiplication. Even though this system was more advanced than the improbable sail-carts pushed by air in the manuscripts of a few of his fifteenth-century predecessors, it was nonetheless based on gears made from wheels and pinions, and the problem of friction would have been too great to be overcome by the operators. The system of the self-propelled vehicle proposed here is based upon the use of springs, a mechanical component Leonardo will carefully analyse in the *Treatise on the Elements of Machines*, and will apply to some of his studies for the wings of the flying machine.

fig. 1
One of Leonardo's most interesting, fascinating and well-known projects is on folio 812r of the Codex Atlanticus. For years it was interpreted as 'Leonardo's automobile', only recently has it revealed its true nature.

fig. 2
A technical image of Leonardo's complicated project.

A

Two large spiral springs underneath the horizontal cogwheels provide the motive power. The springs are enclosed in a wooden drum and are wound in inverse direction. Leonardo often used spring-propulsion systems, especially for watch mechanisms.

The two drive springs, directly connected to the horizontal cogwheels, release the accumulated energy rotating them inversely. The two wheels are coupled and transmit the accumulated energy to other mechanisms on the cart. Their direct coupling excludes any possibility that Leonardo had conceived of a differential mechanism. A single spring would have sufficed to propel the vehicle, however, two springs give a more elegant, symmetrical solution; also, their energy is summed together.

B

The devices on the corners of the cart transmit motion to the wheels as well as setting off a pair of leaf springs that can be seen on the top of the cart. The pins of the two corner wheels rhythmically hit the ends of the two leaf springs. The corner device on the left side represents a system of escapement similar to that used in watches. The system regularises the release of the drive springs. Leonardo is well aware that the energy released by a spring is not constant. In order to avoid a jerky start followed by brusque deceleration, Leonardo equips the cart with an escapement that guarantees a uniform release of power, marked by the rhythmic, audible 'clack' of the pins striking the end of the leaf springs.

C

A small drawing represents a device that is essential for the functioning of the cart: the remote-control handbrake. This consists in a fillet, most likely made of wood, that slips along a moulding. The fillet is pushed into the teeth of the two horizontal wheels. Thus, after the drive springs have been wound, the two horizontal wheels are prevented from rotating and the cart remains stationary. A cord can be attached to the ring in the sliding moulding, the horizontal wheels are released and the cart is put in motion.

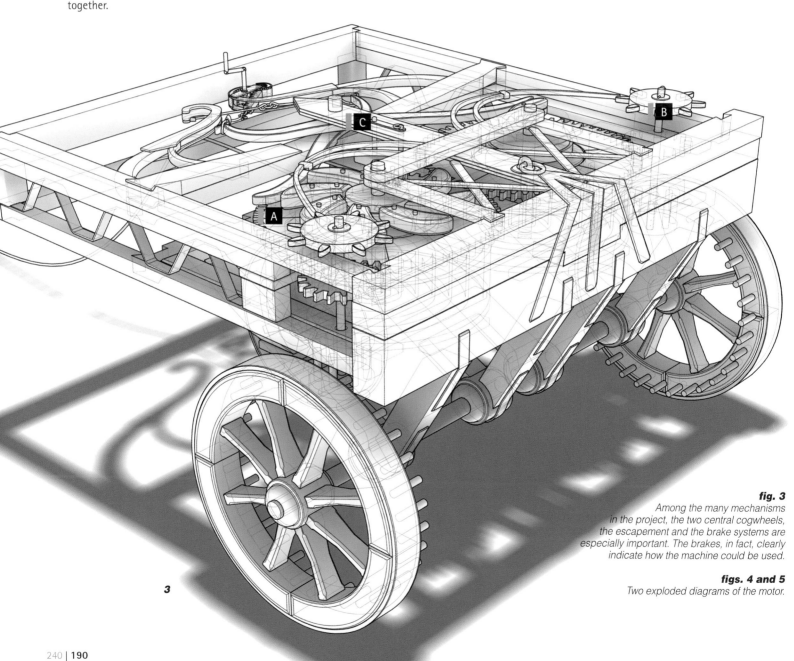

3

fig. 3
Among the many mechanisms in the project, the two central cogwheels, the escapement and the brake systems are especially important. The brakes, in fact, clearly indicate how the machine could be used.

figs. 4 and 5
Two exploded diagrams of the motor.

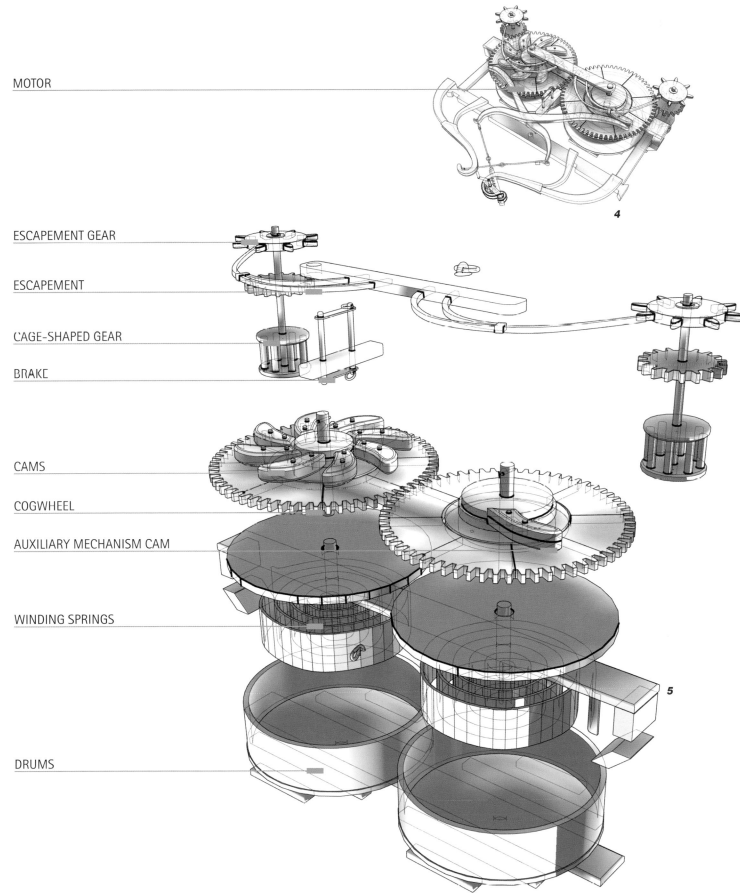

MOTOR

4

ESCAPEMENT GEAR

ESCAPEMENT

CAGE-SHAPED GEAR

BRAKE

CAMS

COGWHEEL

AUXILIARY MECHANISM CAM

WINDING SPRINGS

5

DRUMS

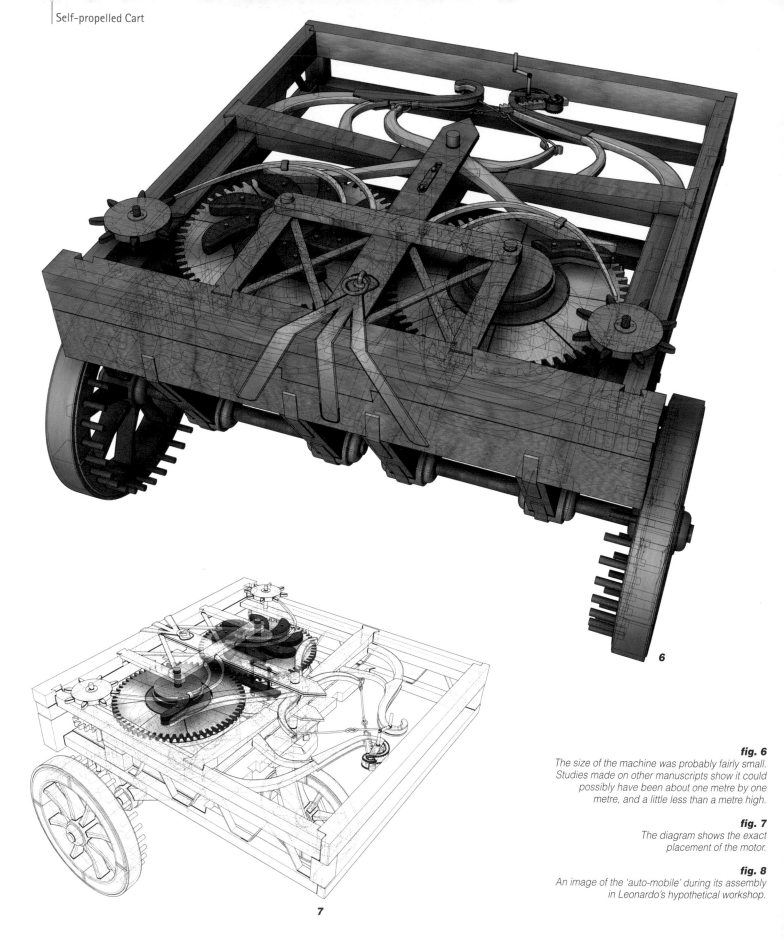

6

7

fig. 6
The size of the machine was probably fairly small. Studies made on other manuscripts show it could possibly have been about one metre by one metre, and a little less than a metre high.

fig. 7
The diagram shows the exact placement of the motor.

fig. 8
An image of the 'auto-mobile' during its assembly in Leonardo's hypothetical workshop.

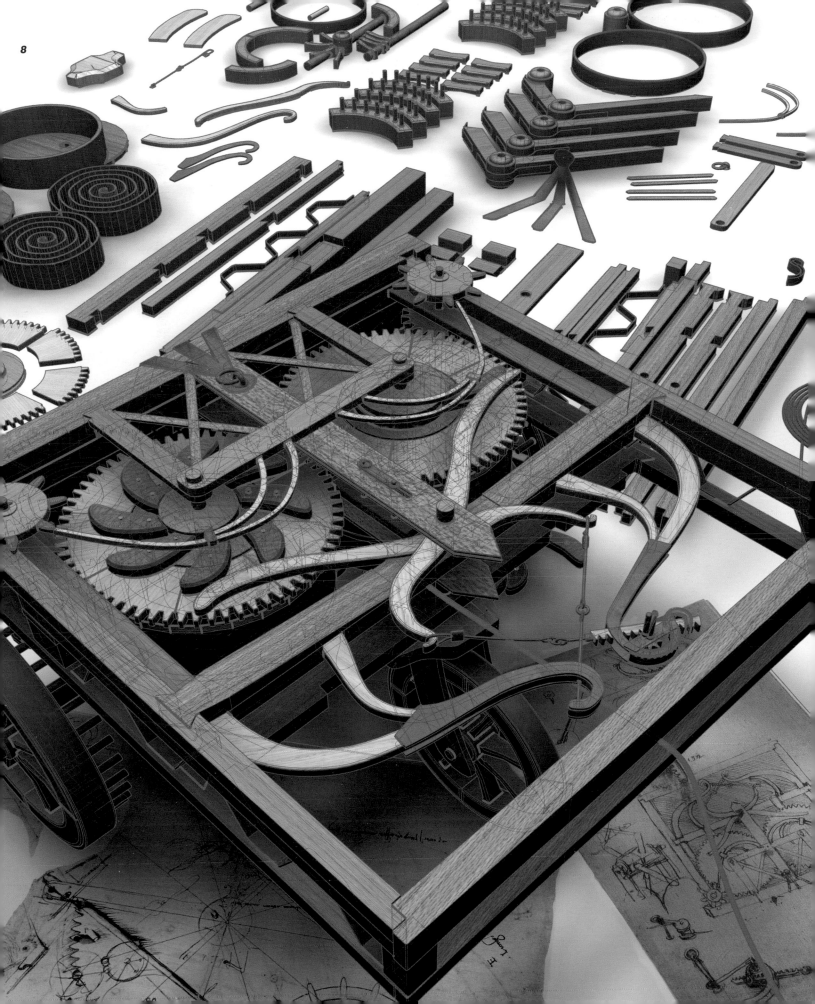

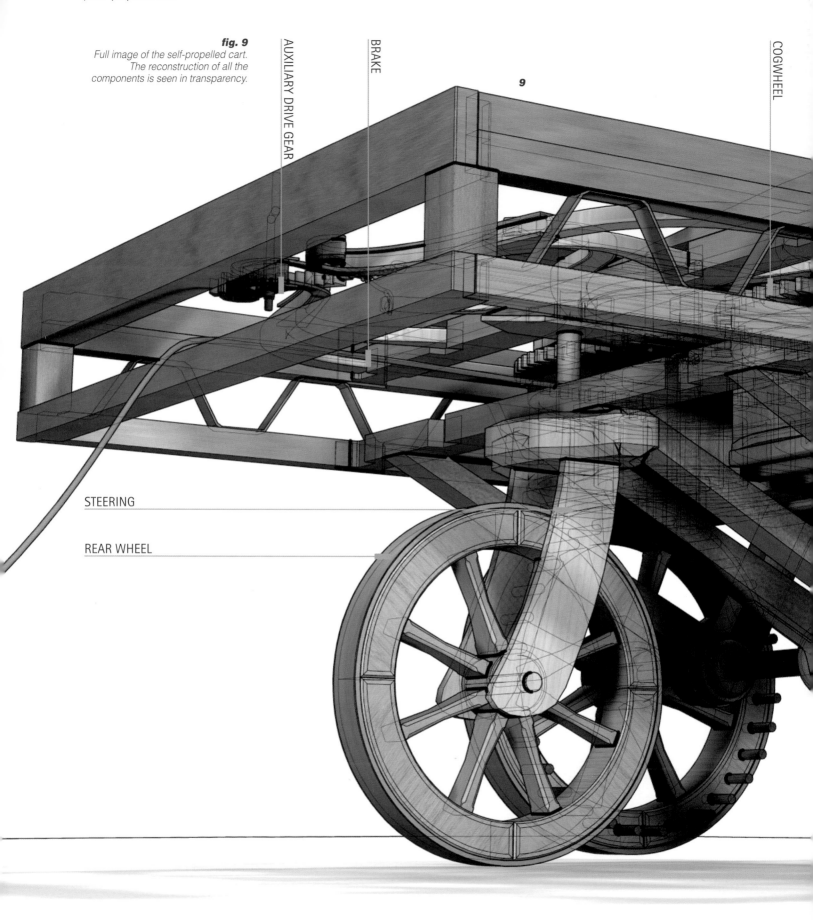

fig. 9
*Full image of the self-propelled cart.
The reconstruction of all the
components is seen in transparency.*

AUXILIARY DRIVE GEAR

BRAKE

9

COGWHEEL

STEERING

REAR WHEEL

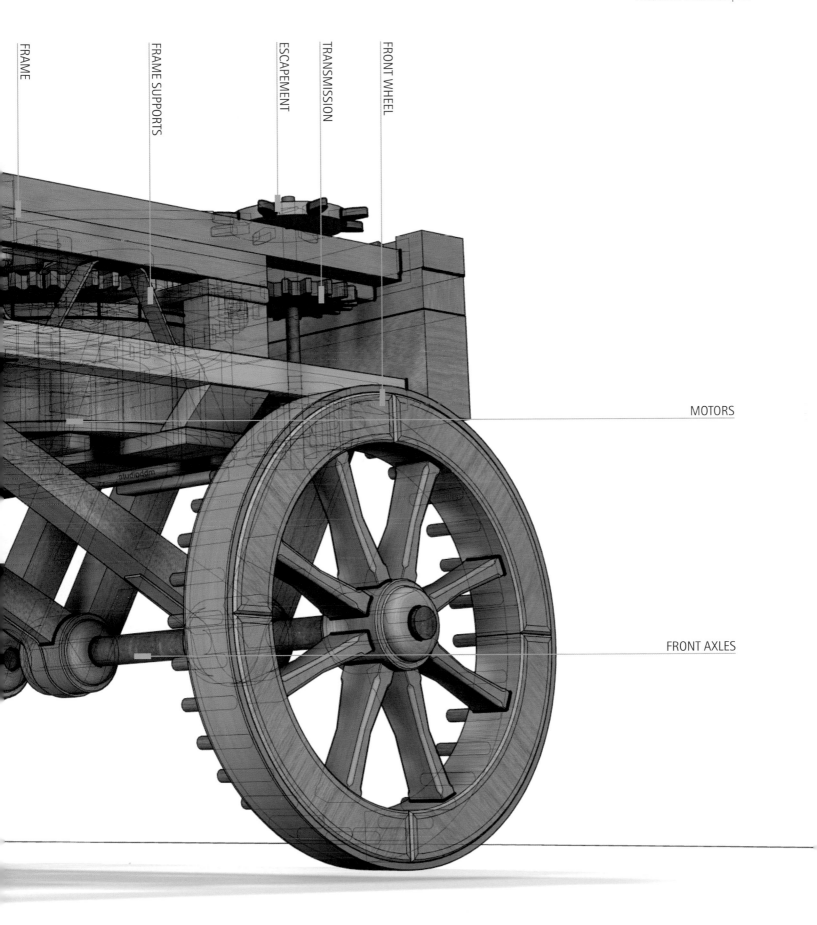

FRAME

FRAME SUPPORTS

ESCAPEMENT

TRANSMISSION

FRONT WHEEL

MOTORS

FRONT AXLES

Vinci, 1452

1460

1470

1480

1490

1500

circa 1507

1510

Amboise, 1519

Codex Arundel, f. 231v

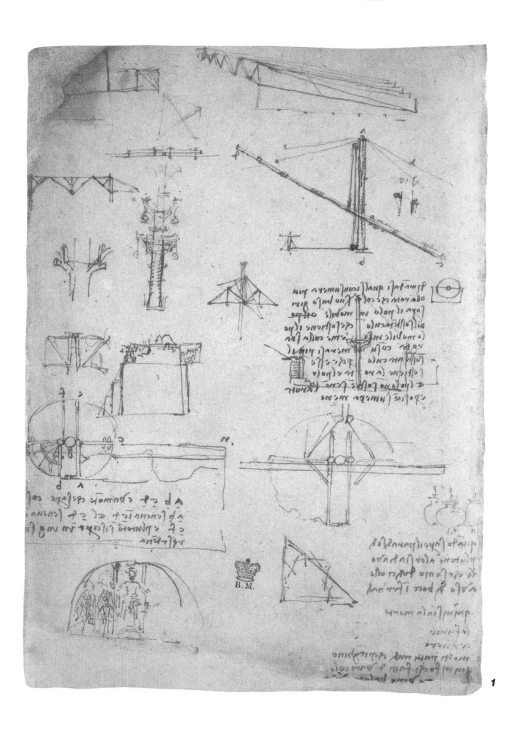

B.M.

Theatrical Staging for Orpheus

Certainly one of Leonardo's most highly appreciated activities in the various courts that enjoyed his presence was the staging of theatrical spectacles. The ephemeral character of these stage settings has left us without one of the most fascinating aspects of his work. One of the very few works for which there is still some trace is the stage setting for the myth of Orpheus, the tale that recounted the unfortunate love between Orpheus and Eurydice. The spectacle was staged during Leonardo's second sojourn in Milan, and thus, for the recently installed French government. Evidently, Leonardo's fame as director of theatrical spectacles for the Sforza had brought the new lords to him. The stage setting designed by Leonardo has been handed down in a series of sketches on two pages of the Codex Arundel, on a page in the Codex Atlanticus and in another that is part of a private collection. Two fragments from this latter page have recently come to light and show drawings for a mountain and female figures, perhaps the Erinyes or Furies swooping down on Orpheus. All these fragments give us a fairly precise idea about the type of staging that Leonardo had in mind. There are two elements characterising the scene: naturalism and dynamism. In order to understand the scope of this project, we should remember that the most successful staging during the Renaissance was the so-called 'perspective stage setting', dominated by a series of urban buildings in perspective. The scene was essentially in perspective and basically static. Leonardo places the dramatic environment of Orpheus in a naturalistic space, with valleys and mountains. Here, the first, bucolic part of the drama unfolds, the courtship of Orpheus and Eurydice. At a certain point, the scene opens up, the mountains fade into the background and from the depths of the earth Pluto emerges with his infernal entourage. The underworld is the setting for the second, tragic part of the tale. Leonardo quite effectively describes this moment of the drama in a note on folio 231v: 'When Pluto's Paradise opens, let there be devils with bellowing infernal voices. Here also Death and the Furies, Cerberus, many naked *putti* who are sobbing; also flames made of various colours [...] that dance about'. Pluto's Paradise is naturally hell, and the whole scene recreates a moment in the myth of the unfortunate love between Orpheus and Eurydice just as Poliziano described in *Orpheus*, a dramatic work that was already renowned for it famous staging in Mantua in 1490.

fig. 1
Interspersed among Leonardo's various codices there are projects for theatrical machines; opposite is a drawing from the Codex Arundel, however, there are others in the Codex Atlanticus and in private collections.

fig. 2
A part of the scenography illustrated in the Codex Arundel and in other codices.

overleaf, following page, fig. 3
Workings of the mechanism on the set. The blue arrow indicates the movement of the machine when weights or two to three people are placed in the container.

fig. 4
Sequence showing the three working phases of the theatrical scene: curtain closed, opening, and completely open, with the appearance of the actor on stage.

fig. 5
Main parts of the theatrical staging.

2

A The sequence of images here shows in simplified form the opening of the theatrical staging. While the play was going on, the dome was part of the mountain scenery. Of course, instead of being perfectly spherical, it could be made in various shapes out of papier mâché and painted very realistically. Also, due to its light weight, it could be constructed with very large dimensions. The models of mountains hid from view the complicated system of pulleys and tie-rods that allowed the whole system to move.

B At the precise moment and with considerable theatrical effect for the times, the entire set opened revealing a second stage. The circular movement of the two enormous domes not only opened onto a new scene, but also brought the protagonist on stage. In fact a platform with the actor 'waiting in the wings' emerged onto the scene.

C Once the two large domes finished their movement they were entirely opened to the public allowing a new acting space for the actors and the new character who had just appeared before the audience.

D The working of the mechanism was very simple. Initially, the actor was in position below the stage on a small platform that worked like a lift. Behind, stage operators were ready to load a container with weights. Once loaded, like a counterweight, the container dropped while at the same time the lifting the protagonist on the platform and moving the entire mechanism opening the domes. Another hypothesis could have been that it was the operators who lowered themselves into the container at the right moment.

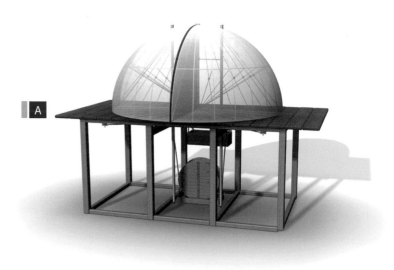

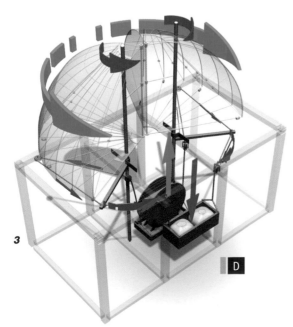

3

4

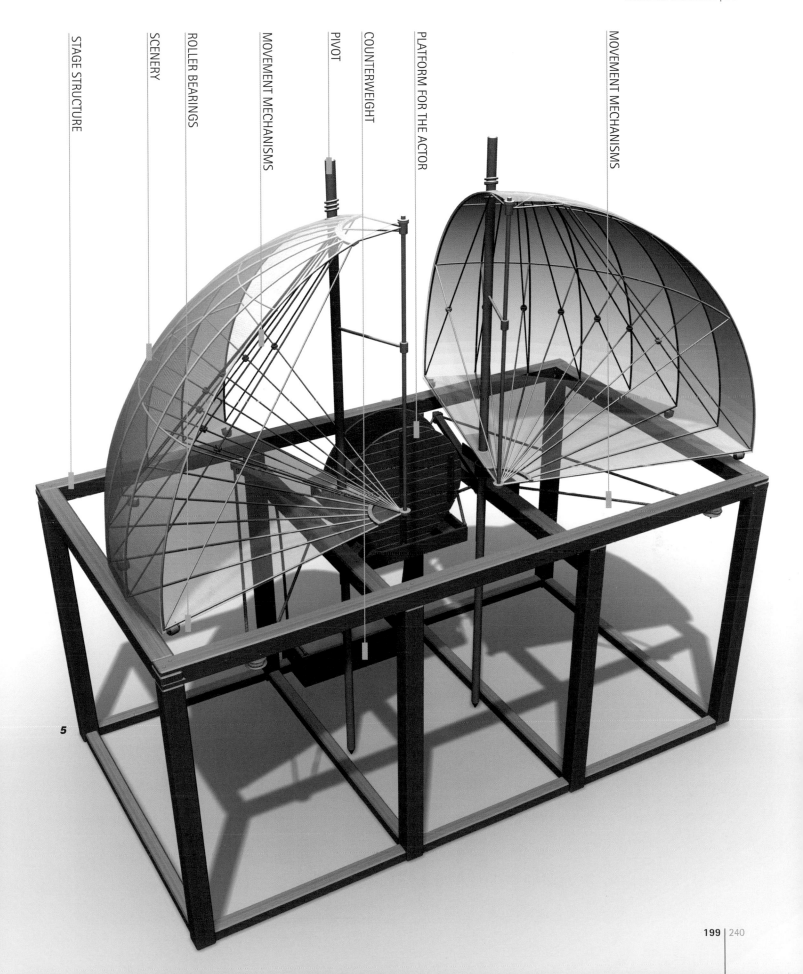

STAGE STRUCTURE

SCENERY

ROLLER BEARINGS

MOVEMENT MECHANISMS

PIVOT

COUNTERWEIGHT

PLATFORM FOR THE ACTOR

MOVEMENT MECHANISMS

5

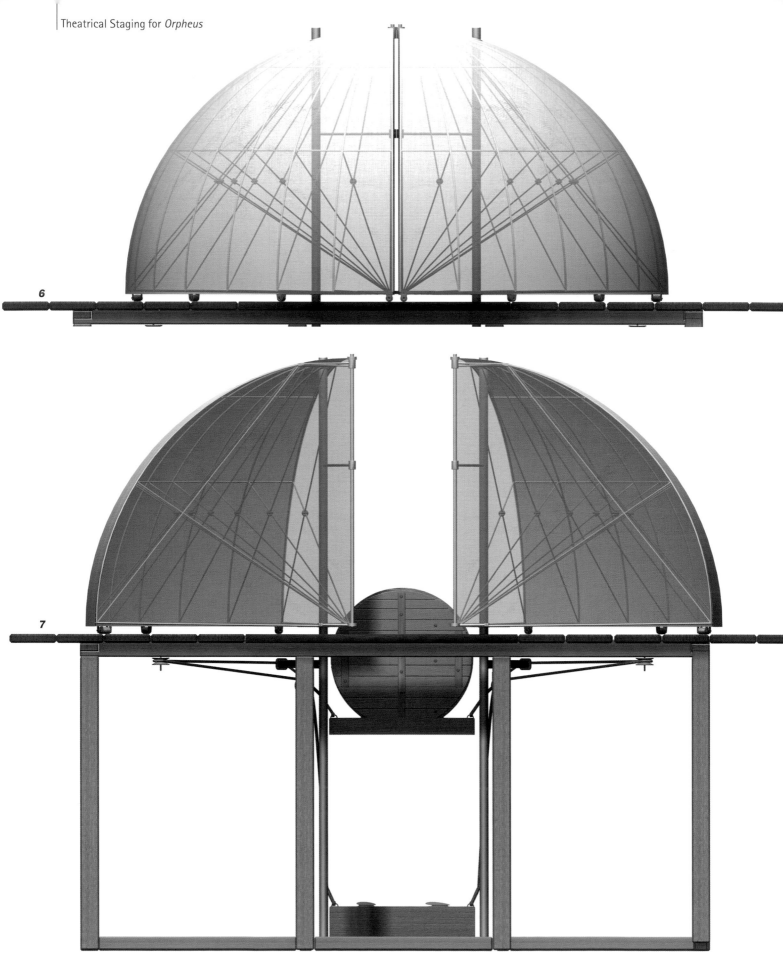

6

7

figs. 6 and 7
The theatrical staging seen from the audience, closed and while opening. On the lower side of the two domes there is a system of roller bearings where the entire structure rested and rolled maintaining the correct trajectory for opening.

fig. 8
A folio that belongs to a private collection where a very explicit drawing of the same project can be seen. The drawings are so clear that it is assumed they were meant for a client or a builder. The details for the pulleys and the system of counterweights moving the lift and going up to the stage can be seen.

COUNTERWEIGHT

SUPPORT STRUCTURE

DETAIL OF A PULLEY

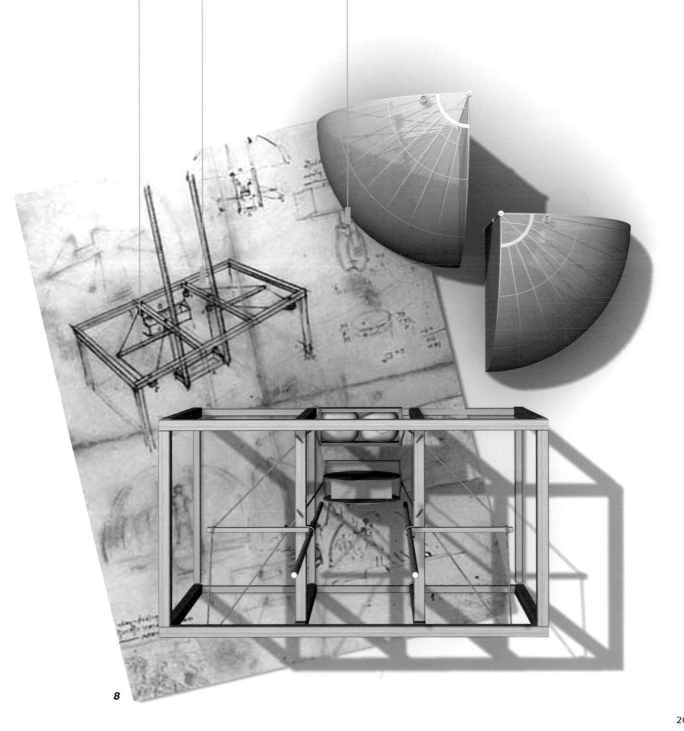

8

Skull-shaped Lyre
Mechanical Drum
Viola Organista

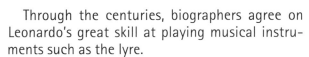

Through the centuries, biographers agree on Leonardo's great skill at playing musical instruments such as the lyre.

Traces of another aspect of Leonardo's work in the field of music also exist. Certainly, there are many reasons why at about thirty years of age, Leonardo leaves Florence and goes to Milan. Nonetheless, it is significant that the biographers of the time tie in his musical activity with his transfer to the capital of the Sforza duchy. Supposedly, Lorenzo the Magnificent gave Leonardo the honour of bringing a lyre he had constructed to Ludovico il Moro. It was a bizarre lyre shaped in the form of a horse's skull and made in silver. In addition to being valuable for its material and originality of shape, as Vasari states, it was made in such as way 'so that the sound should be more sonorous and resonant'. And Vasari adds that he played on this lyre so wonderfully that Leonardo's performance was superior to any other musician at Ludovico's court. Thus, the Sforza duke aware of Leonardo's many abilities kept him in Milan.

Based on what we know from the biographers and the presentation letter written by Leonardo to Ludovico il Moro, his move to Milan which was a fundamental event in his life, was not instigated by his activity as a painter but rather his abilities as musician and inventor of musical instruments, not to mention his activities as military engineer. This is perfectly understandable if we place ourselves in the historical context of the period: war was always at the forefront, and by presenting himself at the Sforza court as a military engineer he would have had more chance of success. In terms of the music, the importance it played in Renaissance courts often takes on surprising dimensions. The princes launched 'acquisition campaigns' in order to employ the most famous composers and musicians. Once they were hired on, they received enormous salaries and sometimes were even recompensed with lands, private incomes and every kind of benefit. At the end of the 1400s, when the Sforza lose their power and are exiled from Milan, Ercole d'Este the Lord of Ferrara, sends his agents to Milan in order to procure the famous musicians in the Sforza musical chapel. After numerous difficulties they succeed in hiring Josquin des Prez. Like many other great musicians of the time, he is a foreigner, and until Monteverdi comes on the scene, music is a field dominated by Northern Europe. Among the great Italian musicians of the fourteenth century is Franchino Gaffurio (1451-1522), and according to one hypothesis, he is the figure portrayed by Leonardo in the painting found today in the Ambrosiana painting gallery. Composer, organist, author of treatises on musical theory (*De Harmonia*), Franchino Gaffurio was active in Milan where he was chapel master in the cathedral. The figure in the portrait by Leonardo is holding a slip of paper with the inscription 'Cant Ang', a possible allusion to one of Gaffurio's famous compositions, the *Angelicum ac divinum opus musicae*. The princes were ready to pay enormous sums for compositions such as this. The fact that Leonardo possibly knew Franchino Gaffurio in still another piece in the relationship Leonardo had with the musical world, a particularly intense relationship during his years in Milan under the Sforza. It should also be remembered that for many years during the 1480s Leonardo was active at the Sforza court not as a painter, but as the director for festivals and spectacles. (The famous *Virgin of the Rocks*, commissioned from Leonardo in 1483, was not initiated by the court but by a private confraternity). The festivals at court may well have included musical interludes, the creation of compositions and the invention of instruments. This seems to confirm what has been handed down through the documents, that at least initially, Leonardo was held in esteem and renown as a musician and machinator rather than a painter and scientist. The musical instruments designed in a codex dating from the period with the Sforza seem to echo this early activity in Milan. One of the instruments from the Ashburnham 2037, formerly part of Manuscript B, shows a lyre in the form of an animal's skull, a direct reference to the instrument attributed to Leonardo as a valuable political homage to the Sforza. Based on what we know, Leonardo was quite original in his designs for constructing the main types of instruments of the period. It is not an easy task to accurately reconstruct the types, variants and uses for musical instruments from Leonardo's time. In the first place, very few original instruments have survived until today. The most useful sources for reconstructing Renaissance instruments are the treatises that, especially during the sixteenth century, are dedicated to music or to individual instruments. The other important source depicts instruments in paintings, the wood marquetry and other types of art from the period.

During the course of the Renaissance, the progressive use of musical instruments and the frequent use of music in every private and public event in the life of the court contribute in stimulating the new invention of musical instruments or modifying already existing instruments.

During Leonardo's time, there were stringed instruments having medieval roots such as the vielle and the rebec (which did not find a place in the newly-born published music) as well as more advanced instruments such as the lira da braccio, and the family of the viols, the viola da braccio and the viola da gamba (as shown in the decoration in Giorgione's house, ca. 1500). Like other instruments, the viols were constructed based on the principle registers of the human voice, soprano, alto, tenor and bass, in families of different dimensions where the smallest instrument was also the highest in tonality. The violin, viola and cello are still used today and are derived from corresponding Renaissance stringed instruments. The lute has the principle role in the other large category of instruments: those with plucked strings. The first music specifically written for the lute was composed and printed in 1507, confirming the lute's primacy among musical instruments. The Arabs imported it into Europe, and the lute was totally assimilated into Western musical culture. Between the end of the fifteenth and the beginning of the sixteenth centuries the instrumental technique used for the lute underwent a radical change: the strings were plucked by the fingertips of the right hand, in addition to a continued use of the plectrum, part of its Middle Eastern inheritance. The use of the fingers in plucking the strings allowed the lute player to play polyphonic music, and for most of the sixteenth century, the lute was strung with six paired courses of strings, tuned in unison or in octaves. Another very popular plucked stringed instrument was the harp. Both the harp and the lute accompanied the court singer, but they were also depicted in religious iconography as instruments in angelic choirs.

There was also a conspicuous use of percussion instruments (drums, tambourines and triangles) for both popular events as well as civil and military feasts and celebrations held at court. Another area that was in evolution was the use of keyboard instruments. In addition to the organ where the sound is produced by air pressure in the pipes, there was the clavichord, the harpsichord, the spinet and the virginal. For these latter, sound was produced by the pressure of the fingers on the keys that in turn indirectly and mechanically vibrated the chords. The very few, but interesting, traces relating to this mechanical 'environment' found in Leonardo's work are from this context. Leonardo develops new, innovative ideas in the areas of string and keyboard instruments with the viola organista, introducing an original use of the keyboard. The mechanisation and emission of rich and varied sounds are also sought after in the area of percussion instruments, as evidenced in a project for a drum found in the Codex Atlanticus (f. 837r). Finally, in the area of wind instruments, Leonardo creates original projects based on older, simpler designs from the Codex Ashburnham 2037, and later, more complex ones in the Codex Madrid II (f. 76r), among which there is a double drone bagpipe worked using the player's elbow.

Vinci, 1452

1460

1470

1480

1485-1487

1490

1500

1510

Amboise, 1519

1

Skull-shaped Lyre

The lyre in the shape of an animal's skull on this folio is stylistically a simple drawing similar to other musical instruments depicted in the manuscript Ashburnham I (formerly part of Manuscript B). If it were not for the fact that they appear in one of Leonardo's manuscripts, it is more than likely they would not have been attributed to the *maestro* from Vinci. The simple style suits the popular character of some of the instruments represented, such as the flutes. Due to its particular form, the lyre not only implies a more sophisticated cultural context, but also evokes a fundamental episode in Leonardo's life: his move from Florence to Milan. Two biographers of the time both report the event with a lyre as the main protagonist. Anonimo Gaddiano (sixteenth century) describes Leonardo's transfer to Milan as follows: 'At thirty years he was sent by the magnificent Lorenzo to the Duke of Milan, along with Atalante Migliorotti, to present to a lyre, being unique in playing said instrument'. This bit of information (that Leonardo was thirty years old) and given the date of his birth (1452), we can deduce that his move to Milan was made in 1482. Leonardo is not alone; with him is a student, a Florentine named Atalante Migliorotti who was also a musician. Years later, he will turn up again in Rome as an architect. According to the anonymous biographer, the move to Milan consisted in a very specific mission, one of cultural-diplomatic relevance: Lorenzo the Magnificent, Lord of Florence, was sending a gift to the Duke of Milan. Not an ordinary gift: but a musical instrument, a lyre. Thus the episode is part of the shrewd political environment of alliances nurtured by Lorenzo the Magnificent. Giorgio Vasari also confirms the episode: the lyre was made of silver, and was constructed by Leonardo himself in the shape of a horse's head. The drawing on the folio here was made by Leonardo some years later and has to do with a similar instrument: the strings are taut between the teeth and the vertebrae of the head of an imaginary animal.

According to the two sources, Leonardo's artistic and musical qualities are behind his trip to Milan. Leonardo did not stop at presenting the gift, but he was also involved in a competition of court musicians and singers. The instrument in question was in fact the lira da braccio, often-called viola, an instrument most often used for a very fashionable diversion in Renaissance courts: poetry improvisation by a musician-poet with musical accompaniment on the lyre. This, too, was a form reborn from classical antiquity: compositions by the *aiodos*, the bards, improvised poets who were the basis for the great Homeric poems.

fig. 1

The folio (for ease in viewing, reproduced here upside-down) presents three drawings for popular instruments, meant perhaps to produce loud noises rather than musical melodies. One of these is a type of lyre made from the skull of an animal.

overleaf, following page,
fig. 2

Images suggesting how the entire instrument may have appeared complete with strings, rudimental keys, and probably, a small soundboard.

Leonardo probably intended the skull-shaped lyre as a theatrical prop rather than a popular instrument. With respect to his other projects for musical instruments, this one is not particularly interesting either technically or musically. The idea of making musical instruments from the organs and bodies of animals dates to prehistoric times. Nevertheless, there may have been a few improvements that the inventor himself may have added. For example, using the cartilage in the palate to interrupt the strings (the frets on the modern guitar), using the teeth as types of rudimental tuning pegs (like on the violin) and using the cranial cavity as a soundboard.

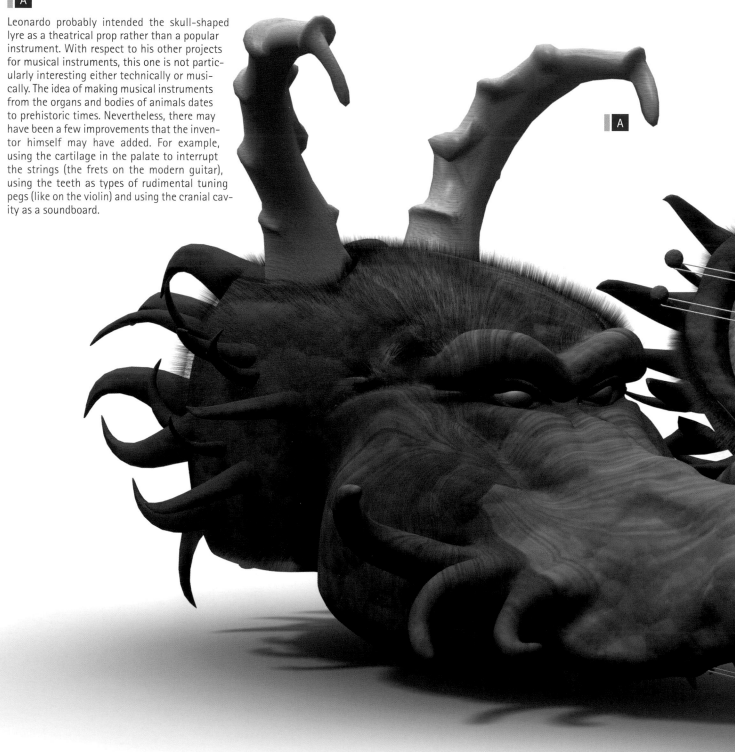

SOUNDBOARD

STRINGS

FRETS

PEGS

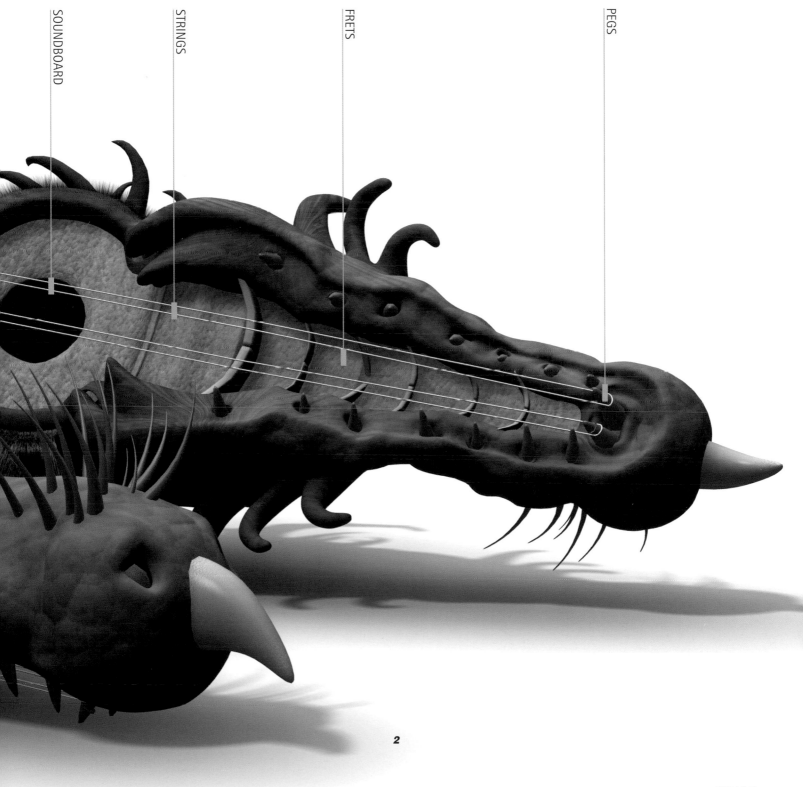

2

Vinci, 1452

1460

1470

1480

1490

1500

1503-1505

1510

Amboise, 1519

Codex Atlanticus, f. 837r

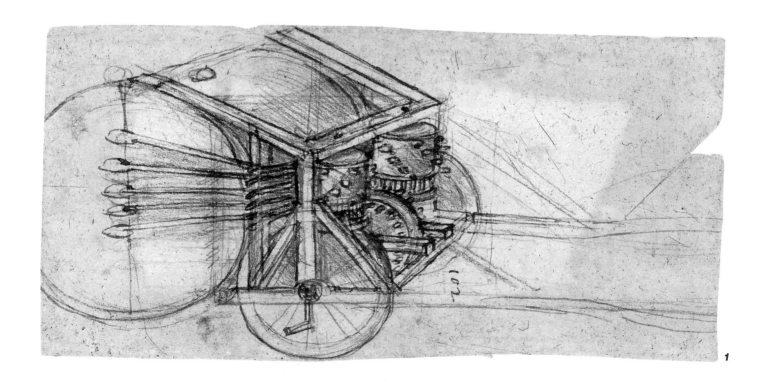

1

Mechanical Drum

2

The drawing of a mechanical drum on this folio is only one of the many examples of Leonardo's studies dedicated to this type of instrument. Percussion instruments are less complex, clearer and perhaps even more useful with respect to stringed instruments (to which he also dedicates much attention). Percussion instruments represent one of the richest chapters in Leonardo's studies on musical instruments. The forms Leonardo proposes are well beyond what was in use at the time, and his research essentially concentrates on two objectives. First, he wants to make an instrument where the timbre and sound can easily be changed at will, using various systems such as transforming and then reversing back the shape and size of the drum, changing the tension on the head, lining up a series of drums, and so forth. Second, he wants to create automatic mechanisms. For the most part, the drawing on this page fragment from the Codex Atlanticus deals with this latter aspect.

Leonardo's strong interest in percussion instruments can not be explained on the basis of the development of musical instruments, a process that will reach maturity during the course of the sixteenth century. Instrumental music increasingly becomes a part of accompaniment for vocal music, and thus creating its own growing autonomy. This development is augmented by treatises dedicated entirely to musical instruments. In these treatises we see a certain marginalisation of percussion instruments. In his treatise *Musica Getutscht* (1511), Virdung even presents the timpani as an invention of the devil, and later treatise-writers, such as Agricola, follow similar lines. It is therefore possible that the amount of space Leonardo dedicates to percussion instruments in his research on musical instruments must be explained in another way: in relation with stage events and pageants, and above all, in relation to use in war. The project appearing on this folio, a sanguine drawing reinforced with ink, probably was destined for this latter arena. On another page from the Codex Atlanticus (folio 877r) there is a series of quick sketches relative to this type of drum. Our drawing is not yet a fully defined composition, but reflects an intermediate stage between a sketch and a finished project. (In general, Leonardo used sanguine more for sketches than for final drawings). The ultimate use for the complex automatic drum was most probably to create a thundering noise in battle. The tone and purpose are reminiscent of various mechanical projects, all bordering on the fantastic, that Leonardo designed for one of the most practised and prized arts of the Renaissance: the art of war.

fig. 1
The original folio presents a very clear, explicit drawing. Careful analysis shows two versions of the same machine; the first has wheels and the second has a crank that substitutes the wheels.

fig. 2
A hypothesis of how the cart may have been used.

A

Leonardo presents two different solutions in the same drawing. The lighter line of the drawn wheels and the right side of the page represent two different configurations for the cart: moveable and fixed. In the mobile version, the cart was pulled by a man whose movement turned the wheels and consequently all the mechanisms connected to them. A toothed wheel in the centre and two large, programmable rollers activated the drumsticks that rhythmically struck the head of the drum. In addition to functioning automatically by the movement of the wheels, the most fascinating aspect of this machine is that it could be programmed. The pegs inserted in the two large rollers could be placed in different beat sequences, thus producing different rhythms.

B

A second interpretation of the drawing places it in a stabile configuration, where there is no movement of the vehicle itself. The various mechanical parts are put in motion by the two levers on the sides, substituting the wheels.

This version of the cart could be used for events in enclosed areas or in situations with limited space where it could not be moved.

fig. 3
Two carts in different configurations: A, pulled version; B, fixed version.

A

DRUMSTICKS

PROGRAMMABLE ROLLERS

CENTRAL WHEEL

SUPPORT FOR THE BEARER

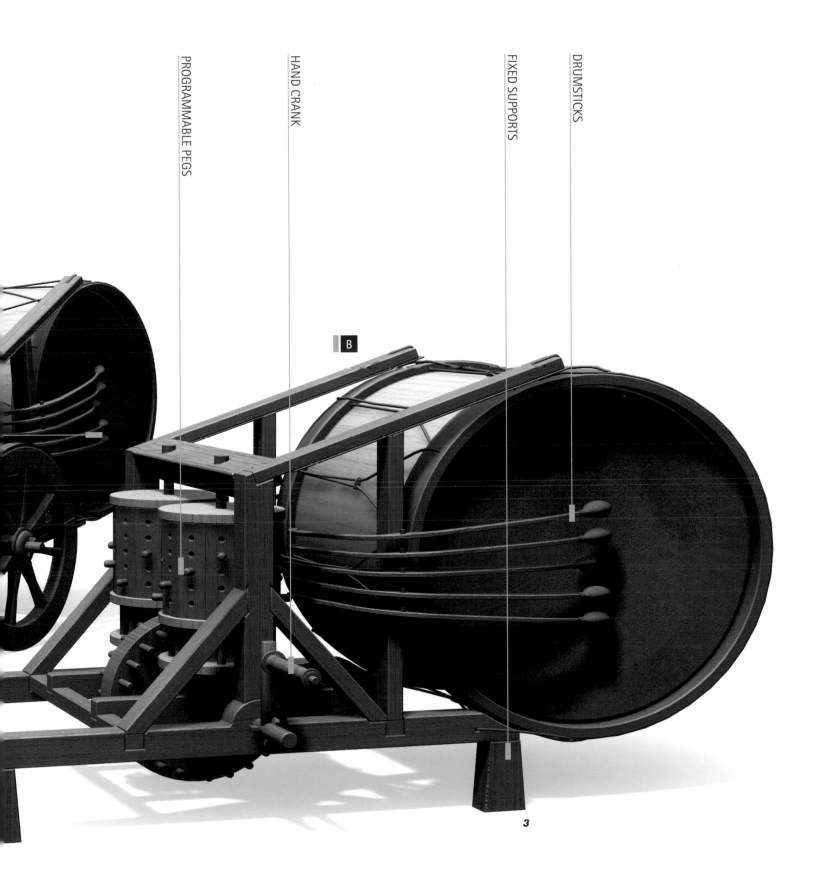

PROGRAMMABLE PEGS

HAND CRANK

FIXED SUPPORTS

DRUMSTICKS

B

3

C The interesting and innovative aspect of this machine is in the automated mechanisms, but especially that the rhythm can be programmed. The 'musician' or the operator who works the mechanism can set the machine to the desired rhythm. Once it is programmed he just has to keep the speed of the motion constant.

The range of the programs was fairly limited. In fact the pegs could be placed in a linear sequence producing a continuous rhythm, or it could be multiplied, simultaneously accentuating one beat rather than another. Naturally, without pegs the mechanism produced no sound whatsoever.

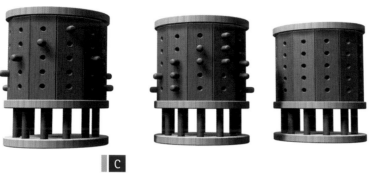

C

fig. 4
Illustration of the mechanisms in motion. The movement of the operator pulling the cart, or turning the hand crank replacing the wheels, puts in motion the large, central toothed wheel attached to the wheel axle. This engages the housing mechanism underneath the programmable rollers. The pegs that can be positioned at different points in holes on the rollers strike the drumsticks rhythmically beating against the head of the drum.

fig. 5
The peg is the part of the cart that can be programmed. Before moving the cart, the pegs are inserted in holes on the rollers in a definite sequence that determines the rhythmic beat.

fig. 6
The programmable roller is divided in two parts: an upper part where the pegs are inserted, and a lower cage-shaped gear that is engaged by the central toothed wheel put in motion by the wheels.

fig. 7
A view of the main parts dismantled.

4

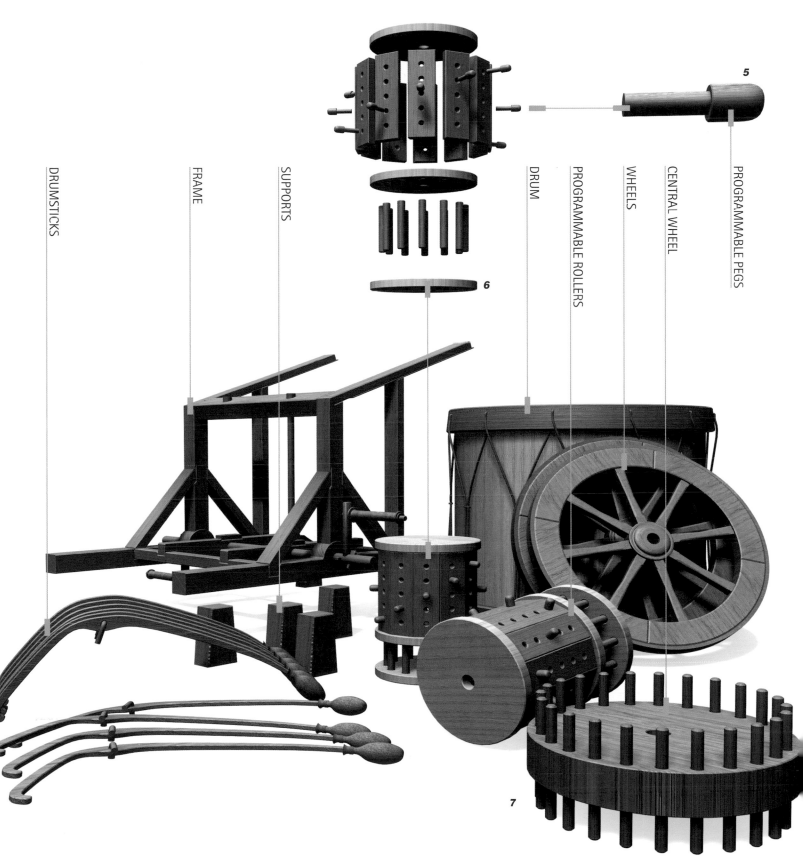

DRUMSTICKS

FRAME

SUPPORTS

DRUM

PROGRAMMABLE ROLLERS

WHEELS

CENTRAL WHEEL

PROGRAMMABLE PEGS

5

6

7

Vinci, 1452

1460

1470

1480

1490

1493-1495

1500

1510

Amboise, 1519

Codex Atlanticus, f. 93r

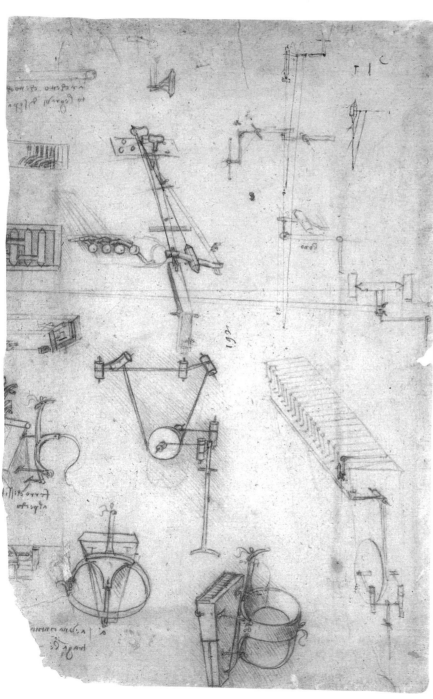

1

Viola Organista

2

Leonardo made these drawings using sanguine or red pencil. Here we find an important change: he goes from the use of pen and ink to using black or red pencil. The general sense of this change, which occurred during the 1490s and became established after 1500, was a move from the crystal clear and rational drawing in pen and ink, to a more pictorial, warmer dimension. This is not a minor detail. All the major artists of the *Cinquecento* prefer to draw in pencil, unlike the practice during prior periods. Pencil permitted greater expression of the new vision of the world, more complex, more sceptical, more metaphorical. This change first occurs with Leonardo, and relates to every area of his studies: scientific to mechanical, as seen in this folio. Nonetheless, it should be pointed out that because these drawings correspond to the beginning of this process, Leonardo uses the sanguine with the clarity of a pen tip.

The various drawings on this folio are almost all related to the same project: an instrument that was well known during the period. In the viola organista the strings were moved mechanically. Leonardo tries to modulate and vary the sound generated by the instrument, and to do this he proposes various hypotheses, none of which is truly complete. One of the studies were the project is more complete is this folio from the Codex Atlanticus where Leonardo includes not only drawings related to the mechanism that would have worked the viola organista, but also details the manner in which the instrument would have been connected to the player's body (drawings on the lower left of the folio). The page is mutilated, and probably originally contained even other studies forming a more complete idea of the workings. A greater synthesis here should not surprise us. During the 1490s, period from which this folio dates, Leonardo reaches a major equilibrium in all areas of his research. This is the period of the sharply drawn mechanical elements from the Codex Madrid I, studies where Leonardo isolates the basic parts of machines (wheels, screws, etc.) following a very theoretical conception of mechanical design. The very clear delineation of the parts in this musical instrument (especially the centre drawing on the folio) recalls this theoretical horizon. Leonardo invents this particular musical instrument putting together mechanical elements: wheels, cords, etc. The close resemblance with other devices (for example, the automatons in human form or the flying machine) can be explained in this way.

figs. 1 and 2
Left, folio 93r in the Codex Atlanticus contains many sketches and projects for a musical instrument. On the lower left there is a fairly complete sketch of the instrument. Above, the way the finished instrument could have appeared.

overleaf, following page, fig. 3
How the player of the instrument might have looked. Leonardo's project allowed the player to walk and play at the same time.

figs. 4 and 5
The instrument as it appears on the folio. In this version the motion lever is placed above; this would limit the use of the instrument making it necessary to work it using one hand on the keyboard and the other keeping the lever moving; this in turn kept the fly-wheel with the horsehair in motion.

3

A In the more complete drawing on the lower right of folio 93r in the Codex Atlanticus the rod appears presumably attached to the right side of the instrument. By using alternating rotary motion, the rod kept the flywheel inside the soundboard moving. It is interesting to note how Leonardo designed this part using different solutions. In fact, in the other parts of the manuscript this 'rod' is oriented towards the lower part of the instrument.

We can imagine that when the player had the instrument harnessed to his body he could activate the rod by moving his legs. By hitting against the lever while he walked, the flywheel would have been in constant motion as well as the internal parts connected to it.

B To carry the instrument a harness was required. The player could easily walk while playing the music, having both hands free.

C The keyboard is similar to one on a piano, and has a three-octave range, enough to play a fairly complex piece. Precisely for this reason, Leonardo seems to try to free up both hands of the operator of the instrument. In fact, the operator's lower limbs generate the energy necessary to put the mechanical parts in motion.

D The soundboard holds the sound-producing mechanisms, the strings and the complicated pressure parts, the filament that produced the sound. Presumably, this filament was made of horsehair like in modern violins. Also inside the case were the mechanical parts put in motion by the alternating movement of the external rod and the flywheel.

BRACES
KEYBOARD
HARNESS
SOUNDBOARD
DRIVE LEVER

4

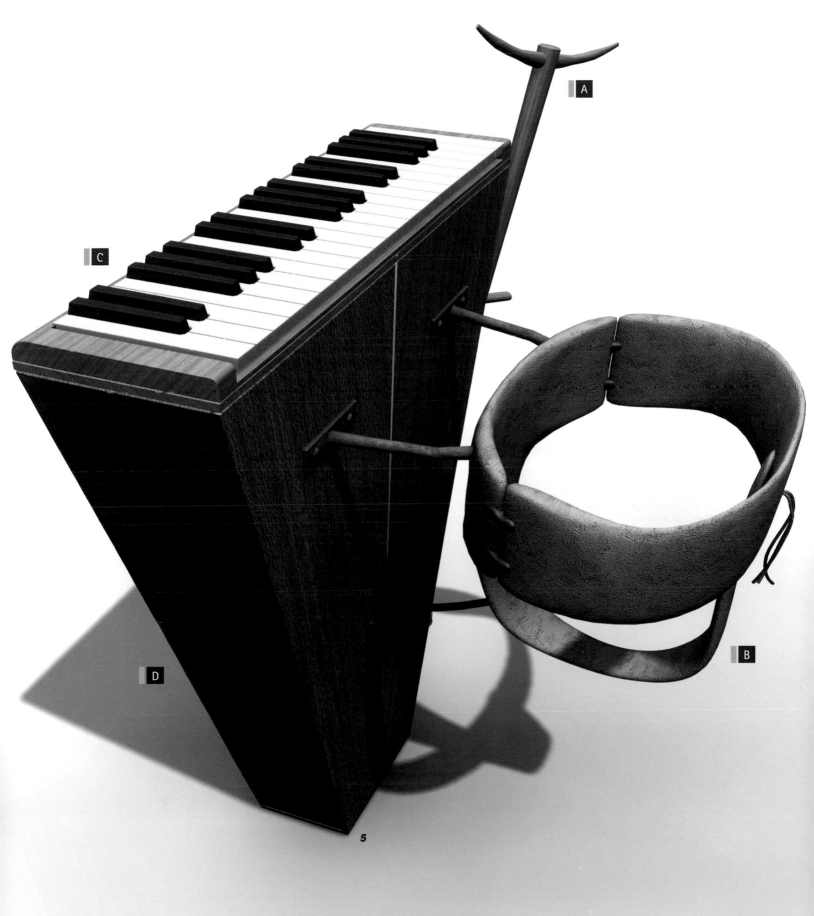

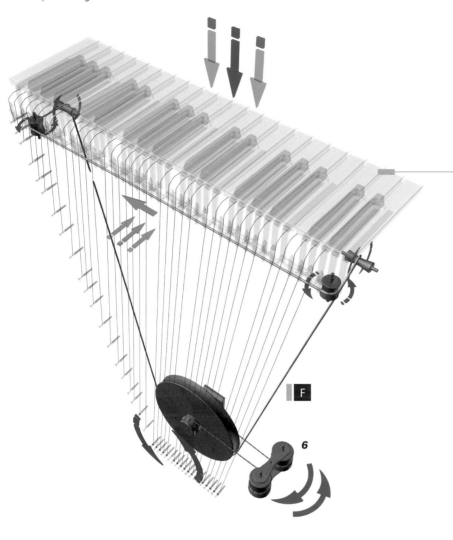

DETAIL OF THE MECHANICS

7

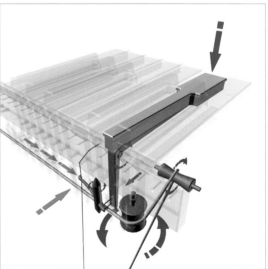

8

6

fig. 6
Detail of the percussion mechanism of the strings.

figs. 7 and 8
Workings of the mechanical parts.

fig. 9
*The viola organista in a more plausible configuration,
with the lever of the rod placed towards the ground.
There must have also been an opening in order to tune
the instrument. The tuning pegs drawn on the upper
part of the manuscript are in fact located
inside the soundboard.*

F The horsehair is put in motion by the alternating movement of the rod, periodically struck by the musician's
legs. Thus, the horsehair has a continuous, one-direction
linear motion. Additionally, it can be presumed that the
flywheel was fairly large and had the necessary inertia to
supply movement to the horsehair for a few seconds.
Pressure on the keys (fig. 9) activated a mechanism that
with a small, precise arm, engaged the string drawing it
near the moving horsehair; the two parts (string and
horsehair) rubbing against each other produce a dynamic
sound, that is proportionally intense to the pressure on
the keys.

E Leonardo probably thought of different configurations for the instrument. In this version the rod lever is placed towards the bottom of the instrument (also in fig. 4). This configuration allows the operator to move the lever, thereby putting in motion all the mechanisms connected to it, simply by walking or marching. Presumably, during a parade the musician could march through the city streets playing with both hands. In fact, the horsehair like a violin produces sound by the rubbing against the strings, and being in constant motion it produces sound every time a string, activated by the keyboard, brushes against it.

HORSEHAIR

FLYWHEEL

'MOTOR'

SUPPORT FOR FLYWHEEL

REMOVABLE COVER

TUNING PEGS

9

DRIVE LEVER

E

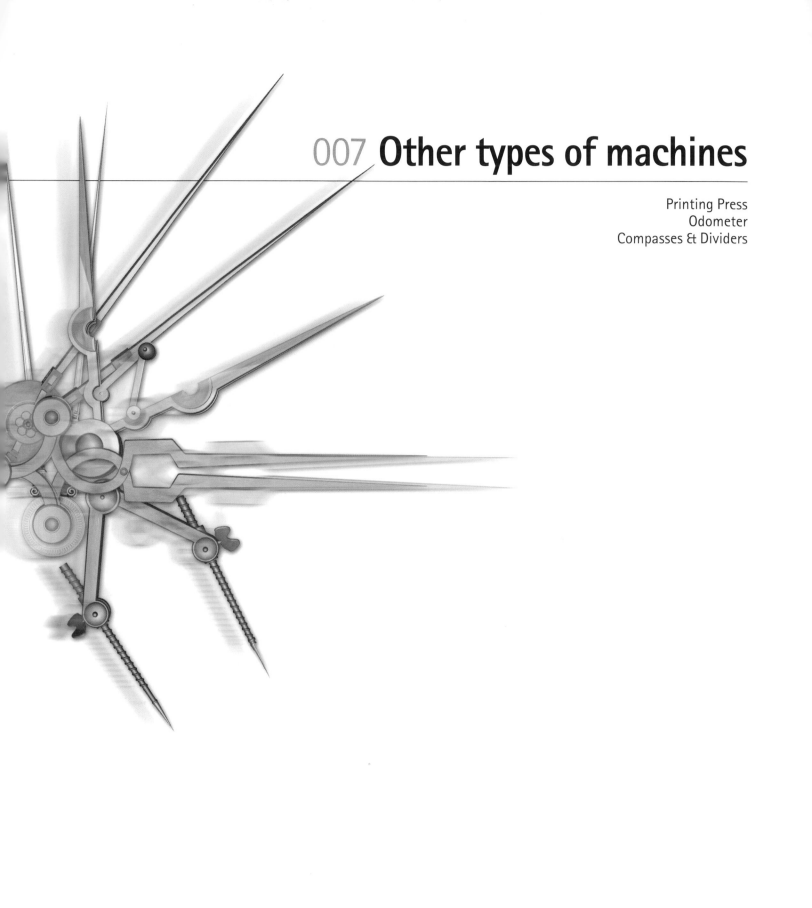

Other types of machines

Printing Press
Odometer
Compasses & Dividers

The Codex Madrid I is comprised of two main parts: projects for machines, and more abstract studies related to the behaviour of weights on inclined planes, the laws of statics and dynamics. The Codex 'On the Flight of Birds' is similarly structured: next to the part dedicated to the study of natural flight as applied to the design of the flying machine, we find a more theoretical section dealing with statics and dynamics.

For many centuries there was a fairly clean-cut division between mechanical theory (the study of statics, dynamics and kinematics) and mechanical design. The former was developed as a fairly abstract discipline. The latter was prevalently empirical in nature. One of the innovations introduced by Leonardo was to try to unify mechanical theory and applied mechanics. The more theoretical sections of the Codex 'On the Flight of Birds' and the Codex Madrid I are not studies for mechanical projects in and of themselves, but are more like appendices or premises on the topics of statics and dynamics that Leonardo often directly applied to the mechanical designs, to the understanding of natural flight.

The other fundamental innovation that Leonardo introduces is to undertake studies that go beyond the single machine meant for this or that specific function. He makes a systematic study of the basic elements that make-up each machine: the screw, the wheel, the spring, the roller, the cords and so forth. Leonardo calls them mechanical elements and in his writings he often refers to a *Treatise on the Elements of Machines*. During the 1960s when two codices by Leonardo where found in Madrid, one of the two, the so-called Madrid I, seemed to some scholars to correspond with the treatise mentioned by Leonardo, otherwise unidentifiable. As seen by the statements made by Leonardo himself, in reality this treatise was structurally much more complex than the Madrid I. It consisted in a broad theoretical part dedicated to geometry, statics, dynamics, kinematics, and a more practical part dedicated to the simple elements of every machine (wheels, screws, etc.), true machines in and of themselves.

The study of the fundamental elements common to every machine is part Leonardo's general attitude towards research. For example, in anatomy he also makes comparative studies where a series of comparisons emerges between humans and animals, or between various animal species in order to identify the fundamental and shared biological traits.

By uniting theoretical and practical mechanics, as well as his thoughts on mechanical elements, Leonardo attempted to give machine design a technical status, overcoming the centuries-long distinction between mechanical and liberal arts. Historically, the term 'mechanical arts' indicated all human activities using the hands, from painting to goldsmithing, from sculpture to construction engineering. Everything that was based on manual work was considered culturally and socially inferior. There were problems connected with this for physicians and surgeons, for example, who laboured throughout the Middle Ages to see their discipline brought to the dignity of a science, founded not only on the intellect but also on use of their hands. During the course of the *Quattrocento* the painters, sculptors, engineers try to vindicate the scientific component of their work. Through the study of the laws of geometry used for perspective in order to correctly represent space, the study of anatomy in order to naturalistically depict bodies, the study of proportion in order to create harmonious figures, the painters and sculptors give a scientific foundation to their art. By the first half of the 1400s, the engineers were transformed from artisans to authors of treatises, and with his writings Leonardo puts the crowning touch on this process of cultural emancipation.

Leonardo raises machines and their components to a theoretical dimension that becomes even more evident with the extreme accuracy of his drawings, for their intellectual and demonstrative value. This emerges in the passages Leonardo dedicates to mechanical elements, a field more consonant to traditional science. As we read in this passage on screws: ' Here the nature of the screw is demonstrated and how it should be used in pulling as well as pushing; and how it is stronger single rather than double, and thinner rather than thicker, when being moved by equal lever lengths and equal force. And some discussion will be made of the number of ways to use it and how many endless types of screws there are [...] and on the nature of its threads [...]'. Leonardo is describing a simple screw, and even so, previously a description so highly elevated in tone and structure had been reserved only for theoretical subjects such as Aristotle's laws of statics or dynamics. Leonardo approaches the study of the dynamic properties in springs in the same manner, submitting this mechanical element to quantitative considerations on the relationship of time, motion and force, which up to that point had been considered in topics such as light, water and more general dynamic forces.

From the 1490s on, Leonardo fine-tuned the theoretical direction he took in mechanical design. Subsequent refinements continued until years later they were expressed in written thoughts entitled *De' poli* (On Poles) dealing with friction, or, envisioned as a full treatise or book with the title *De confregazione* (On Friction), which at one point Leonardo declared he would like to write. The complex theoretical dimensions of Leonardo's mechanical designs are not always so explicit. In this regard, his project for a pedometer (Codex Atlanticus, f. 1rb), a device for counting the number of steps covered on foot, is a good example. Another project appearing on the same page shows an odometer, an instrument for calculating distance covered, which probably had a specifically practical purpose given the frequent measurements made around the walled fortresses Leonardo constructed as military engineer for Cesare Borgia. It is also probable that the pedometer also had similar practical uses. Nonetheless, the idea of measuring and quantitatively analysing an action made by the human body, such as walking, emerges more or less at the same moment that Leonardo is studying the human body and the systematic geometric analysis of its movements (as seen in the drawing found in the Codex Huygens dating from the sixteenth century, but inspired by lost studies made by Leonardo).

Obviously, practical use is a horizon that Leonardo tries to keep in sight even in his most theoretical studies. For example, in the studies in the Codex Madrid I dedicated to the elements of machines, the ultimate goal of his analysis of pulleys and tackles is to increase the efficiency of the force needed to lift heavy weights. Many of the analyses he made on the wheel are also directed towards similar ends, and with the invention of the system there is also its immediate practical use preventing the wheel turning in the wrong direction (the ratchet wheel, or as Leonardo calls it, 'servant').

There is also a third dimension in Leonardo's mechanical design. Often there is an aesthetic dimension alongside the practical and theoretical aspects. In addition to being intelligent and useful, machines are at times also beautiful. His designs for dividers and compasses are among some of the most spectacular examples. These instruments had a specifically practical use, especially important in Leonardo's own studies. Nonetheless, for some of these objects, technological research goes hand-in-hand with its aesthetics. For example, one of the requirements in compass-design was that once opened it remains in a fixed position. For this to happen the friction between the two legs had to increase with the increase in the arc; this could be accomplished by increasing the number of hinges. As seen in the drawings in the Codex Atlanticus, f. 48 recto and verso, Leonardo not only meets this objective but he uses it as an opportunity to give the compass heads an original and elegant shape. An enormously fascinating leg of the trip, called – and rightly so – 'from the minor arts to industrial design'.

Vinci, 1452

1460

1470

1478-1482

1480

1490

1500

1510

Amboise, 1519

Codex Atlanticus, f. 995r

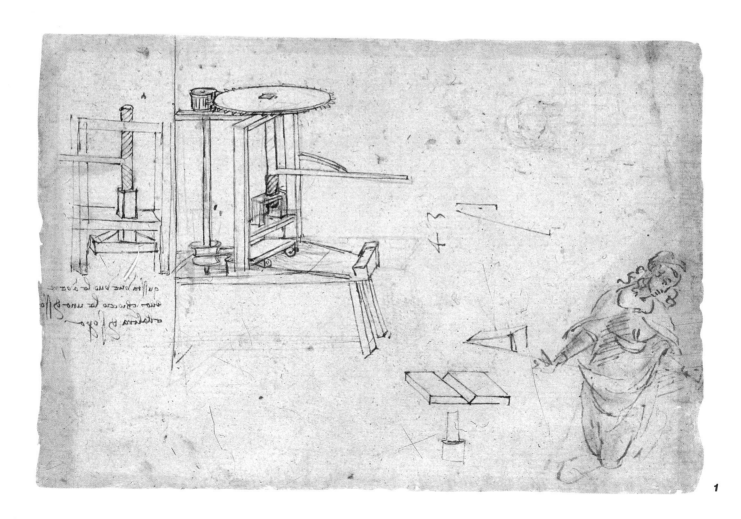

1

Printing Press

2

This folio could be compared to a still from a video on the cultural environment in which the young and promising artist from Vinci found himself in the vibrant city of Florence during the *Quattrocento*. The folio is fragmentary: the original sheet could have contained other notes and drawings. It is noteworthy that next to the drawing of a Madonna there is a project for a printing press. It is not certain that the former drawing is by Leonardo. This doubt is evidenced in the direction of the hatched lines on the bust of the Virgin, going from upper right to lower left; Leonardo was left-handed and his hatched lines usually went in the opposite direction. In favour of a positive attribution to Leonardo is the strength of the drawing itself, delineated with a few, nervous lines and the Virgin's expression and pose. Even if the attribution of the drawing is uncertain, the presence of an artistic study alongside an engineering study is important. It would be normal in a workshop such as Verrocchio's, to find military arms and bells cast next to sculpture pieces. For a person in the Renaissance, the idea of art covered both aspects, while science dealt with all types of theoretical knowledge. The scientific emancipation aspired to by many artists was not in associating mechanical inventions with artistic creations, but rather the basic theoretical research (the scientific research) of both these activities.

Florentine artistic workshops around the 1470s are in fibrillation due to the appearance of the first printing presses. Other than a few private initiatives, it is the Dominican monks at Santa Maria Novella in 1476 who set up a printing-house. This event is not out of context seeing that the convents of the time were the principal means for the diffusion of culture in the form of costly manuscripts. The introduction of the moveable-type press and the use of paper rather than parchment allowed more economical books to be produced. This facilitated access to culture by the superior classes of artisans, which in the most advanced cases, hoped to give a scientific foundation to their manual activity. Leonardo's curiosity about printing is therefore comprehensible. In printing as in other fields, he attempts to increase the level of automation saving both time and labour. Even though we have no proof that Leonardo did in fact print some of his sheets, later on, in an anatomical page from Windsor Castle (no. 19007v), he poses the problem of how to most faithfully print his drawings, preferring the more costly but precise copper-etching technique rather than wood-cuts, or xylography. The possibility that one of the studies in the Codex Madrid II (f. 119r) represents an original system of simultaneously printing text and images is also under debate.

fig. 1
Two distinct projects can be seen in Leonardo's drawings. On the right there is a mechanical press worked with a single lever. In the drawing on the left Leonardo has sketched a variation of the same machine with a double worm screw; it is interesting to note the analogy of the latter with the mechanisms he studied and developed for the flying machine.

fig. 2
The mechanism of the lever that activates a worm screw and the press.

CAGE-SHAPED GEAR

WORM SCREW

TOOTHED WHEEL

INCLINED BED

FIXED BED

MECHANICAL LEVER

VERTICAL PULLEY

MOVEABLE BED

SHEET OF PAPER

A

When the operator moved the mechanical lever the gears where put into motion and the machine carried out various movements. The press was slowly lowered by the worm screw and printed the sheet of paper placed under the carriage. A large toothed wheel on the upper part of the press moved the other mechanisms in addition to a vertical pulley. A line was wound around it and attached to a moveable carriage. When the mechanism was put in motion the pulley wound in the line, causing the carriage and page to be moved closer to the press. When this process was finished, the carriage returned and the press lifted.

B

Leonardo drew a curve close to the lever, made probably of wood, that presumably could be used both as a guide and a rest for the motion of the lever, or, perhaps also meant as protection for the operator. The printing process could also be fairly repetitive and forceful, and the force exerted by the operator must have been fairly intense. A reason for this type of bulkhead may have been to keep the body away from the machine during the printing.

C

An interesting aspect of the machine is the moveable bed. As in many later versions of the typographical press, the page is brought under the press without the use of hands. A carriage with small wheels slides along the bed of the structure, and pulled by a line and a pulley activated by a single mechanical lever, it is lifted up to the press. When the press itself is only a few centimetres from coming in contact with the page, the carriage stops. Once the page is printed, the carriage slides back to its initial position with the printed sheet. All this is accomplished in a single movement by a single operator.

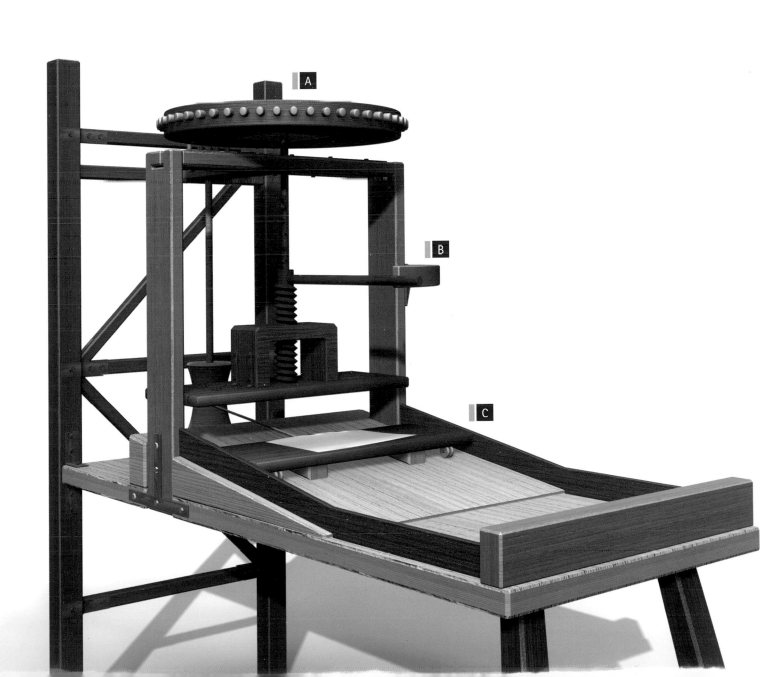

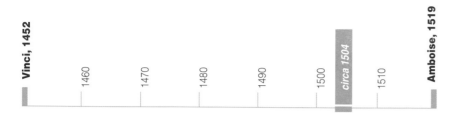

Vinci, 1452

1460
1470
1480
1490
1500
circa 1504
1510
Amboise, 1519

Codex Atlanticus, f. 1br

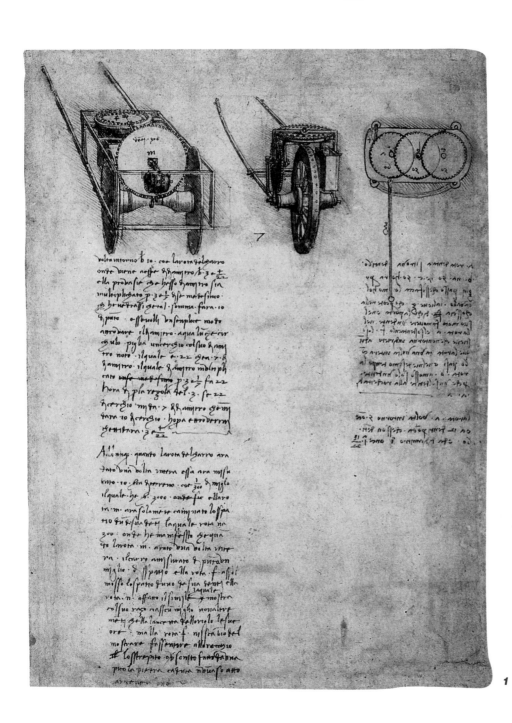

1

Odometer

2

This folio contains one of Leonardo's most complete presentations for a mechanical project. The very clear style of the drawings, the text arranged in two regular columns, the writing (at least in the left-hand column) following the conventional style (left to right); all contributing to an unusual dimension in Leonardo's work: a page ready for publication, in manuscript or printed form. A plausible hypothesis? This problem also surfaces in the studies for mechanical elements found in the Codex Madrid II. Leonardo dealt with typographical problems, and in the margins of an anatomical page from around 1510, mentions a printing technique capable of faithfully reproducing the complexity of his designs. Nevertheless, there is no certain answer. It could be that Leonardo presented the graphic elements for these studies so clearly for a specific reason, such as a demonstration for a patron interested in odometers (counting of the miles covered by a cart) and pedometers (number of steps walked). There is an underdrawing demonstrating that Leonardo first sketched in the drawings and then went over and refined them, a usual procedure for presentation drawings, meant to be used out of the context of private notes. This manner of presentation, however, did not endure. The note underneath the pedometer on the right side of the page is written in Leonardo's usual right-to-left handwriting, certainly not an easy read. It may well be that Leonardo added the drawing and note on the right at a later point in time. The drawing of the pedometer is drier and more schematic than the other projects. It is possible that once he had presented the two projects on the left, Leonardo decided to use the available space for a new drawing, more consonant with his own personal study and thus free from worrying about some form of publication.

The beauty of the two drawings is remarkable. We can appreciate the optimal use of hatching with the use of ink wash, the two main techniques used for defining the form and enhancing the volume of figures. Here they are combined to render accurate every detail. The two drawings of an odometer deal with the mechanical nucleus of the device attached to a cart. As elsewhere, the hatching points up the analytical nature of the projects, and their parts dismantled from the whole and waiting to be assembled. Leonardo has set a theoretical nucleus, a fundamental device (in two variations) that can be applied to individual concrete situations, and for the cart drawn on the folio 855v in the Codex Atlanticus.

fig. 1
Two projects for odometers are on this folio; the third is a drawing for a pedometer.

fig. 2
The most important element of this project for Leonardo was the large central wheel on the odometer; all the holes in the disk contained pebbles that fell into a container below once the wheel finished its rotation.

A

The odometer is an instrument for measuring distances. There are different types, ranging from very small sizes used to measure distances directly on a topographical map, to very large dimensions. In Leonardo's project, the odometer resembles a cart. The operator pulled the cart directly over the territorial distance to be measured.

The vertical wheel transmitted the movement of the cartwheels to the various other mechanisms. When the main axle rotated the large wheel engaged with a worm screw mounted on the axle itself. The toothed wheel activated a front cage-shaped gear and two small toothed wheels mounted on the rear of the odometer. The function of this gear was clearly to activate the large, central wheel. The movement of the rear mechanism, however, can be open to interpretation. Presumably, the teeth in the lower gear train hit against small metallic rods attached to the frame, producing a regular ticking sound indicating the correct functioning of the device.

B

The most interesting component of the cart is the central wheel. A series of holes made internally were constantly filled with markers, probably simple pebbles or small wooden spheres. Each time the wheel completed a turn, a marker fell through the single hole, falling into a container below. Once the entire distance for measurement had been covered, the operator only had to count the pebbles in the box and calculate the length of the area covered.

C

The frame was a simple, fundamental structure. While the odometer was in use, it is presumed that an animal or person drew the vehicle while an operator, walking alongside, continually filled the holes in the central wheel with markers. Naturally, each hole held a single marker at a time.

D

There was a large container attached to the frame, into which the markers dropped each time the central wheel completed one full turn. The longer the distance to measure, the more the box filled up.

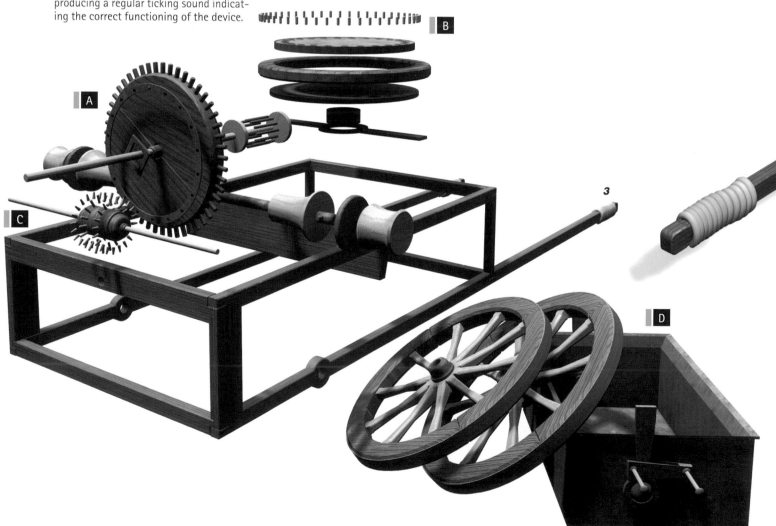

fig. 3
A view of the dismantled odometer.

fig. 4
The main components of the assembled odometer.

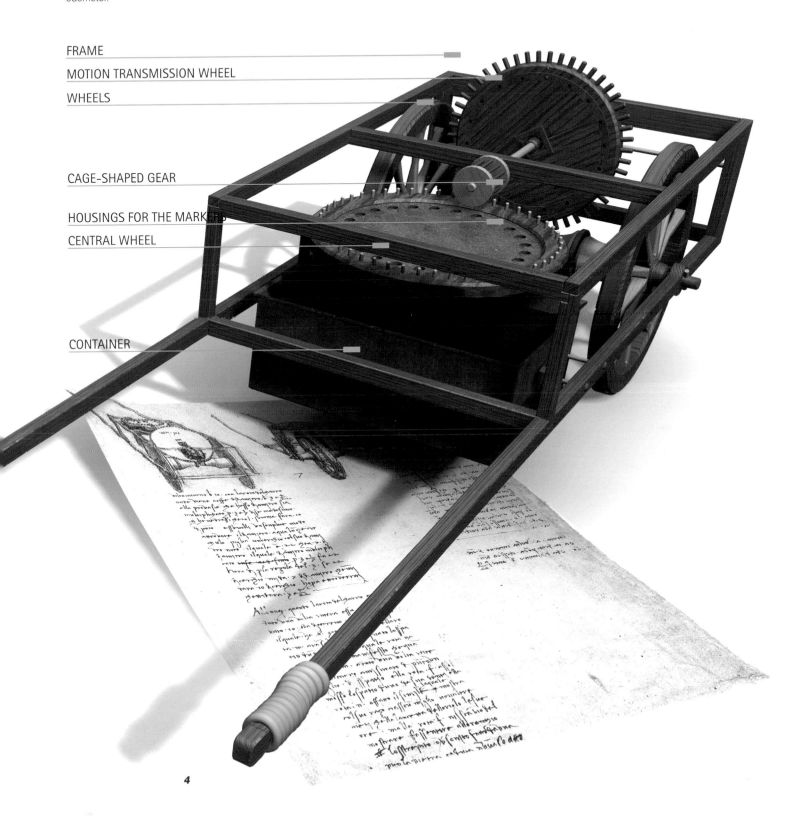

FRAME

MOTION TRANSMISSION WHEEL

WHEELS

CAGE-SHAPED GEAR

HOUSINGS FOR THE MARKERS

CENTRAL WHEEL

CONTAINER

4

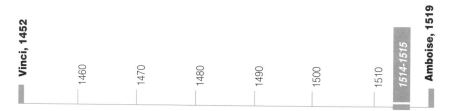

Vinci, 1452

1460

1470

1480

1490

1500

1510

1514-1515

Amboise, 1519

Codex Atlanticus, f. 696r

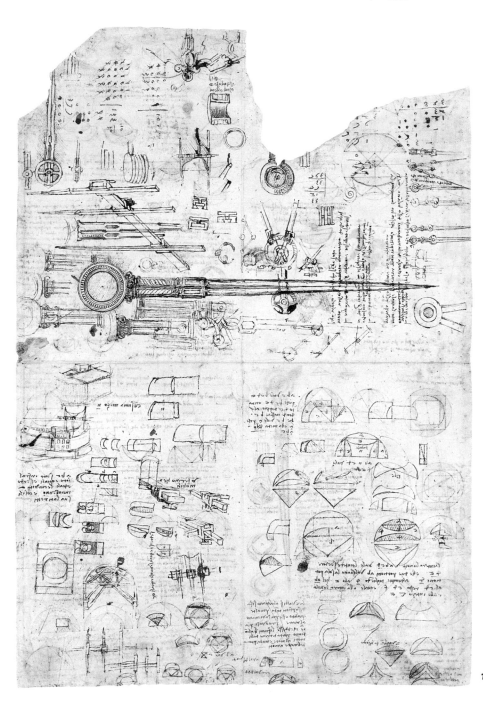

1

Compasses & Dividers

2

This folio from the Codex Atlanticus is a miscellany of notes typical of Leonardo's later years. Geometric studies are intertwined with architectural and engineering projects. For example, on the lower left there is the study for a roof truss, similar to those made while he was in Rome, where not far from his studio in the Vatican the new St Peter's Basilica was under construction. In the upper portion of the folio there are numerous studies for compasses and dividers. The main drawing and most of the smaller drawings deal with simple, two-legged compasses or dividers, but there is also a beam compass consisting in two sliding points on a long, horizontal beam. One of the most fascinating aspects of so many of Leonardo's inventions is the marriage between aesthetic form and function, especially in the design of arms and artillery and work objects. Many designs for lance heads or projects for cannons have such a richness and variety in shape and form that at times the game of 'inventing' goes well beyond practical ends. The same is seen with the design for work tools, such as the compasses and dividers shown here. It is possible that Leonardo actually made and used some of these instruments (for example in describing the circle with the human figure in the drawing of the *Homo Vitruvianus*, there are still evident marks left from the compass that were traced over in pen). The large drawing of a two-point compass or divider on this folio of the Codex Atlanticus is one of the most beautiful. The purpose of the project is to guaranty the stability of the instrument once the legs were open by increasing the contact surface of the hinge points or even their number. The latter system is shown in some of the secondary drawings on the page but in both cases, the technical device becomes a point of departure for creating hinges and joints with odd and interesting shapes and configurations. Research on the functional efficiency of the instrument becomes a springboard for its aesthetic elaboration, almost in the spirit of industrial design. The main drawing of the two-point compass on this folio was copied in a manuscript, today found at the Marciana Library in Venice, containing drawings by Lorenzo della Golpaia and his son, Benvenuto. Lorenzo was a well-known engineer working in Florence, and he certainly knew Leonardo because they both were on the commission to decide where to place Michelangelo's statue of the *David*. It is interesting to note the curiosity that this famous engineer had for, what we would consider today, a minor aspect of Leonardo's work; but one that nonetheless could still astonish an illustrious contemporary.

fig. 1
A page where the drawings for dividers and compasses are mixed together with architectural drawings. The uniting of technical-scientific knowledge and aesthetic considerations in the design for a working tool like the compass makes this page especially interesting.

fig. 2 and following pages
Some hypotheses for dividers and compasses designed by Leonardo.

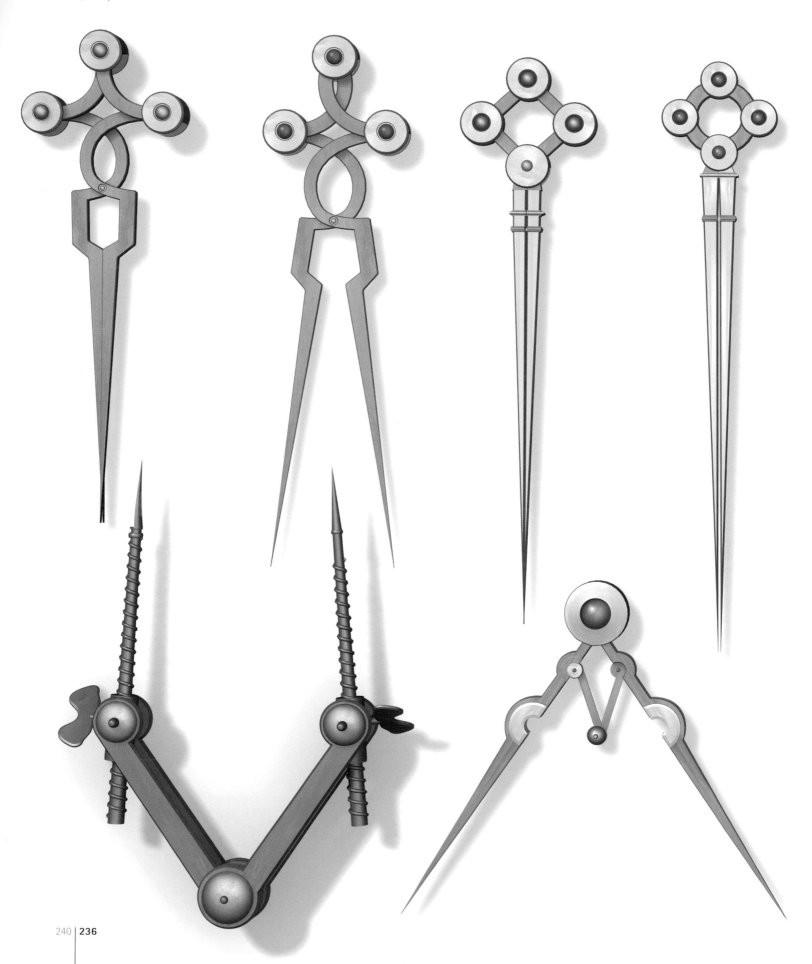

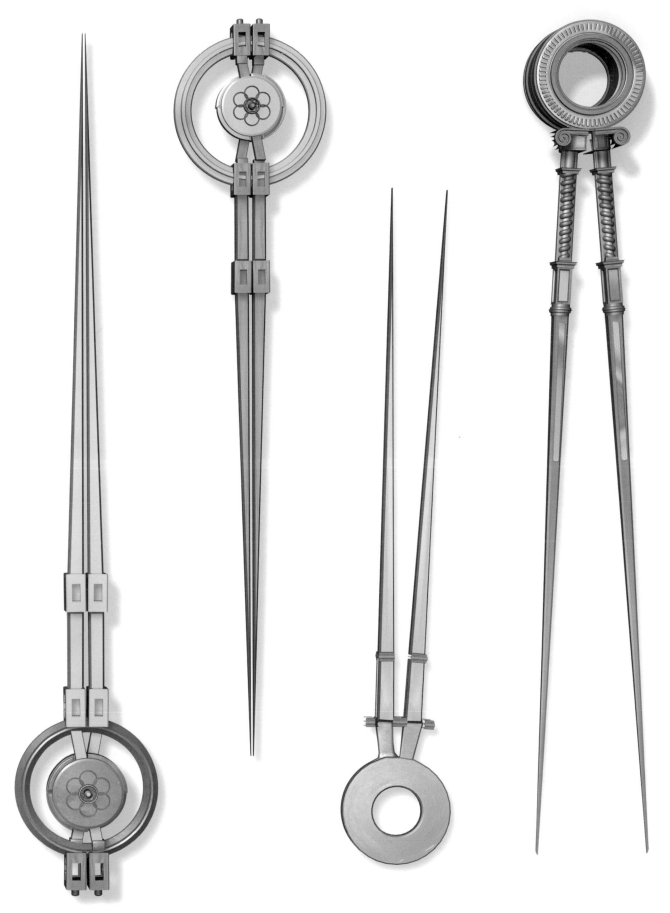

Bibliography

T. Beck, *Beiträge zur geschichte des Machinenbaues,* Berlin, 1900 (1st edition 1899).

L. Beltrami, *Leonardo da Vinci e l'aviazione,* Milan, 1912.

F. M. Felhaus, *Leonardo der Techicher und Erfinder,* Jena, 1913.

I. B. Hart, *Leonardo da Vinci as a pioneer of aviation,* 'The Journal of the Royal Aeronautical Society', XXVII, London, 1923, pp. 244-269.

I. B. Hart, *The Mechanical Investigations of Leonardo da Vinci,* London, 1925, (re-edited in Idem, *The World of Leonardo da Vinci,* London, 1961).

R. Giacomelli, *Leonardo da Vinci e il volo meccanico,* 'L'Aerotecnica', VI, 1927, pp. 486-524.

R. Marcolongo, *Le invenzioni di Leonardo da Vinci. Parte prima, Opere idrauliche, aviazione,* 'Scientia', 41, 180, 1927, pp. 245-254.

R. Giacomelli, *Les machines volantes de Léonard de Vinci et le vol à voile, Extr. du tome 3 des Comptes rendus du 4.me Congrès de navigation aérienne tenu à Rome du 24 au 29 octobre 1927,* Rome, 1928.

R. Giacomelli, *I modelli delle macchine volanti di Leonardo da Vinci,* 'L'Ingegnere', V, 1931, pp. 74-83.

R. Giacomelli, *Progetti vinciani di macchine volanti all'Esposizione aeronautica di Milano,* 'L'aeronautica', 14, 1934, 8-9, pp. 1047-1065.

R. Giacomelli, *Gli scritti di Leonardo da Vinci sul volo,* Rome, 1936.

G. Canestrini, *Leonardo costruttore di machine e di veicoli,* Milan-Rome, 1939.

A. Uccelli, *Leonardo da Vinci. I libri di meccanica,* Milan, 1940.

R. Marcolongo, *Leonardo da Vinci artista e scienziato,* Milan 1950, pp. 205-216.

C. Zammattio, *Gli studi di Leonardo da Vinci sul volo,* 'Pirelli', IV, 1951, pp. 16-17.

A. Uccelli (with the collaboration of C. Zammattio), *I libri del volo di Leonardo da Vinci,* Milan, 1952.

I. Calvi, *L'ingegneria militare di Leonardo,* Milan, 1952.

L. Tursini, *Le armi di Leonardo da Vinci,* Milan, 1952.

M. R. Dugas, *Léonard de Vinci dans l'histoire de la mécanique,* in *Léonard de Vinci et l'expérience scientifique au xvie siècle,* Congress Proceedings, 1952, Paris, 1953, pp. 88-114.

C. Pedretti, *Macchine volanti inedite di Leonardo,* 'Ali', 3, 1953, 4, pp. 48-50.

C. Pedretti, *Spigolature aeronautiche vinciane,* 'Raccolta Vinciana', XVII, 1954, pp. 117-128.

C. Pedretti, *La machine idraulica costruita da Leonardo per conto Bernardo Rucellai e i primi contatori ad acqua,* 'Raccolta Vinciana', XVII, 1954, pp. 177-215.

C. Pedretti, *L'elicottero,* in *Studi Vinciani,* Geneva, 1957, pp. 125-129.

L. Reti, *Helicopters and whirligigs,* "Raccolta Vinciana", XX, 1964, pp. 331-338.

I. B. Hart, *The world of Leonardo da Vinci man of science, engineer and dreamer of flight,* London, 1961, pp. 307-339.

B. Gille, *Les ingénieurs de la Renaissance,* Paris, 1964.

M. Cooper, *The Inventions of Leonardo da Vinci,* New York ,1965.

C. H. Gibbs-Smith, *Léonard de Vinci et l'aéronauthique,* 'Bulletin de l'Association Léonard de Vinci', 9, 1970, pp. 1-9.

Leonardo, edited by L. Reti, Milan, 1974.

Leonardo nella scienza e nella tecnica, Atti del simposio internazionale di storia della scienza (Florence-Vinci 1969), Florence, 1975, pp. 105-110.

C. Pedretti, *The Literary works of Leonardo da Vinci edited by J. P. Richter. Commentary,* 2 vols., Oxford, 1977.

G. Scaglia, *Alle origini degli studi tecnologici di Leonardo,* 'Lettura vinciana', XX, 1981.

Leonardo e l'Età della Ragione, edited by E. Bellone, P. Rossi, Milan 1982.

E. Winternitz, *Leonardo da Vinci as a musician,* New Haven-London, 1982.

Laboratorio su Leonardo da Vinci, exhibition catalogue, Milan, 1983.

Leonardo e gli spettacoli del suo tempo, exhibition catalogue edited by M. Mazzocchi Doglio, G. Tintori, M. Padovan, M. Tiella, Milan, 1983.

M. Tiella, *Gli strumenti musicali disegnati da Leonardo,* in *Leonardo e gli spettacoli del suo tempo,* exhibition catalogue edited by M. Mazzocchi Doglio, G. Tintori, M. Padovan, M. Tiella, Milan, 1983, pp. 87-100.

M. Tiella, *Strumenti musicali dell'epoca di Leonardo nell'Italia del Nord,* in *Leonardo e gli spettacoli del suo tempo,* exhibition catalogue edited by M. Mazzocchi Doglio, G. Tintori, M. Padovan, M. Tiella, Milan, 1983, pp. 101-116.

Leonardo e le vie d'acqua, exhibition catalogue, Milan, 1984.

P. C. Marani, *L'architettura fortificata negli studi di Leonardo da Vinci. Con il catalogo complete dei disegni,* Florence, 1984.

C. Hart, *The prehistory of flight*, Berkeley, 1985.

M. Carpiceci, *Leonardo. La misura e il segno,* Rome, 1986.

P. Galluzzi, *La carrière d'un technologue*, in *Léonard de Vinci ingénieur et architecte*, exhibition catalogue, Montréal, 1987, pp. 80-83.

M. Kemp, *Les inventions de la nature e la nature de l'invention*, in *Léonard de Vinci ingénieur et architecte*, exhibition catalogue, Montréal, 1987, pp. 138-144.

M. Cianchi, *Le macchine di Leonardo da Vinci,* Florence, 1988.

G. P. Galdi, *Leonardo's Helicopter and Archimedes' Screw: The Principle of Action and Reaction,* 'Achademia Leonardi Vinci', IV, 1991, pp. 193-201.

Prima di Leonardo. Cultura delle macchine a Siena nel Rinascimento, exhibition catalogue edited by P. Galluzzi, Siena, 1991.

M. Pidcock, *The Hang Glider,* 'Achademia Leonardi Vinci', VI, Florence 1993, pp. 222-225.

P. Galluzzi, *Leonardo da Vinci: dalle tecniche alla tecnologia*, in *Gli Ingegneri del Rinascimento da Brunelleschi a Leonardo da Vinci*, exhibition catalogue, Florence 1996, pp. 69-70.

D. Laurenza, *Gli studi leonardiani sul volo. Spunti per una riconsiderazione*, in *Tutte le opere non son per istancarmi. Raccolta di scritti per i settant'anni di Carlo Pedretti,* Rome 1998, pp. 189-202.

C. Pedretti, *Leonardo. Le macchine,* Florence, 1999.

D. Laurenza, *Leonardo: le macchine volanti*, in *Le macchine del Rinascimento*, Rome, 2000, pp. 145-187.

S. Sutera, *Leonardo. Le fantastiche macchine di Leonardo da Vinci al Museo Nazionale della Scienza e della Tecnologia di Milano. Disegni e modelli*, Milan, 2001.

Leonardo, l'acqua e il Rinascimento, edited by M. Taddei, E. Zanon, text by A. Bernardoni, Milan, 2004.

D. Laurenza, *Leonardo. Il volo,* Florence, 2004.

D. Laurenza, *Leonardo: il disegno tecnologico,* in E. Bellone, D. Laurenza, P. C. Marani, *Breve viaggio nell'universo di Leonardo,* Genoa, 2004, pp. 25-50 and 69-91.